CGP is <u>No.1</u> for KS3 Science!

It's a long way to the top of Year 9 Science. Luckily for you, this ace CGP Workbook goes the distance from topic to topic.

Each section has stacks of practice that builds your confidence by starting off easier and getting tougher. There are even plenty of maths and practical questions included to help develop the key skills needed for GCSE Science.

We've also added a chunk of test-style practice to check you've mastered it all and full answers for every question. No wonder we're the best — by miles!

CGP — still the best! ☺

Our sole aim here at CGP is to produce the highest quality books — carefully written, immaculately presented and dangerously close to being funny.

Then we work our socks off to get them out to you — at the cheapest possible prices.

Contents

Contents

Published by CGP

Editors: Luke Bennett, Charlotte Burrows, Emma Clayton, Katie Fernandez, Daniel Chesman, Daniel Fielding, Paul Jordin, Charles Kitts, Rachel Kordan, Rachael Rogers, Camilla Sheridan and Caroline Thomson.

Contributors: Ian Connor, David Martindill, Kate Reid, Helen Ronan and Jamie Sinclair

With thanks to Emily Smith for the copyright research.

With thanks to Philip Armstrong, Ian Francis, Glenn Rogers, Charlotte Sheridan and Jamie Sinclair for the proofreading.

ISBN: 978 1 78908 265 4

Graph of carbon dioxide concentration in the atmosphere used on page 70 from the Scripps CO2 program
http://scrippsco2.ucsd.edu/data/atmospheric_co2/primary_mlo_co2_record
Citation: C. D. Keeling, S. C. Piper, R. B. Bacastow, M. Wahlen, T. P. Whorf, M. Heimann, and H. A. Meijer, Exchanges of atmospheric CO_2 and $^{13}CO_2$ with the terrestrial biosphere and oceans from 1978 to 2000. I. Global aspects, SIO Reference Series, No. 01-06, Scripps Institution of Oceanography, San Diego, 88 pages, 2001.
http://escholarship.org/uc/item/09v319r9

Clipart from Corel®
Illustrations by: Sandy Gardner Artist, email sandy@sandygardner.co.uk
Printed by Elanders Ltd, Newcastle upon Tyne.

Based on the classic CGP style created by Richard Parsons.

How To Use This Book

- Place the book on a <u>flat</u> surface ensuring that the text looks like <u>this</u>, not ~~ƨ̣iɥʇ~~.
- In case of emergency, press the two halves of the book together <u>firmly</u> in order to close.
- Before attempting to use this book, familiarise yourself with the following <u>safety information</u>:

Each topic starts with <u>Learning Objectives</u>, telling you exactly what's coming up in the next few pages.

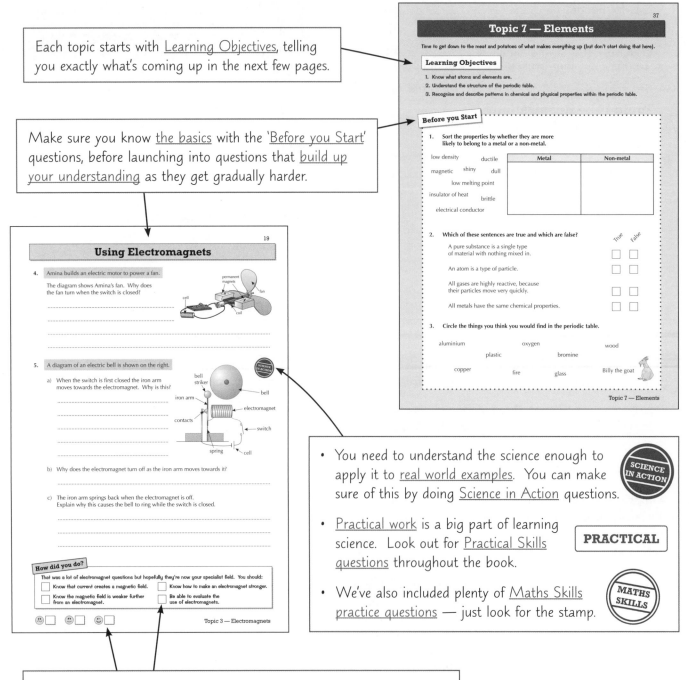

Make sure you know <u>the basics</u> with the '<u>Before you Start</u>' questions, before launching into questions that <u>build up your understanding</u> as they get gradually harder.

- You need to understand the science enough to apply it to <u>real world examples</u>. You can make sure of this by doing <u>Science in Action</u> questions.

  SCIENCE IN ACTION

- <u>Practical work</u> is a big part of learning science. Look out for <u>Practical Skills</u> <u>questions</u> throughout the book.

  PRACTICAL

- We've also included plenty of <u>Maths Skills</u> <u>practice questions</u> — just look for the stamp.

  MATHS SKILLS

Use the <u>topic checklist</u> to mark how <u>happy</u> you are with each <u>key point</u>. Then tick the face that matches how you're feeling about the topic as a <u>whole</u>. Keep going back over what you <u>don't know</u> until you <u>do</u>.

Once you've done all the topics, have a go at the <u>Mixed Questions</u> (p100-104). They'll check you can answer test-style questions on <u>content</u> from the <u>whole book</u>.

You'll find <u>maps</u> online showing where each <u>topic</u> of the <u>AQA Syllabus</u> and the <u>National Curriculum</u> for <u>Key Stage Three Science</u> are <u>covered</u> in this range of Targeted Workbooks. Just head over to: www.cgpbooks.co.uk/ks3scienceresources

Topic 1 — Pressure and Upthrust

I'd hate to force you to learn anything, but this topic is pretty exciting — jump straight in...

Learning Objectives

1. Be able to use the formula to calculate the pressure acting on a surface.
2. Understand that atmospheric pressure decreases with height.
3. Understand that pressure in liquids increases with depth.
4. Be able to explain the effect of upthrust on an object.

Before you Start

1. **Connect the words with the correct definitions and units**

    | mass | | the amount of stuff in an object | | newtons (N) |

    | weight | | the force of gravity on an object | | kilograms (kg) |

2. **Calculate the weight of a book with a mass of 2 kg on:**

    a) Earth (gravitational field strength of 10 N/kg)

    .... N

    b) Mars (gravitational field strength of 3.8 N/kg)

    .... N

    c) The Moon (gravitational field strength of 1.6 N/kg)

    .... N

3. **Circle any examples of forces.**

    friction   air resistance   relative motion

    distance   water resistance

    power   frequency   reaction force

Pressure Basics

1. True or False:

	True	False
a) Pressure measures the force applied to a certain area.	☐	☐
b) Pressure is measured in newtons.	☐	☐
c) Pressure is area divided by force.	☐	☐
d) If a force acts over a larger area, the pressure will be smaller.	☐	☐
e) If a larger force is applied to the same area, the pressure will be smaller.	☐	☐

2. Complete these pressure calculations. **MATHS SKILLS**

a) Calculate the pressure exerted on the ground by a roller that applies 22 000 N of force over an area of 1.1 m².

.... N/m²

b) Calculate the pressure exerted on the ground by a snail that applies 0.3 N of force over an area of 0.0005 m².

.... N/m²

3. Zac accidentally steps on an iron nail sticking out of a floorboard. **MATHS SKILLS**

a) Zac weighs 600 N. 50 N of Zac's weight acts downwards on the point of the nail, which has an area of 0.00001 m². Calculate the pressure exerted on him by the nail.

.... N/m²

b) During a school trip to the local science museum, Zac volunteers to lie down on a bed of nails, which he is told is perfectly safe.

i) Calculate the total area of the nails in contact with Zac, if the pressure exerted by each nail is 37 500 N/m².

.... m²

ii) Each nail point has an area of 0.00001 m². How many nails are in contact with Zac?

....

Pressure Basics

4. Different types of shoe cause different pressures on the ground due to the area they have in contact with the ground.

a) Shiv is doing a sponsored walk in the Arctic. He weighs 740 N. When he is stood on both feet taking a photo of a polar bear, he exerts a pressure of 37 000 N/m² on the ground. Calculate the area of his boots that are in contact with the ground.

.... m²

b) The polar bear that Shiv sees weighs 4900 N. Each of its paws has an area of 0.07 m² in contact with the ground.

    i) What is the total area of the polar bear's paws in contact with the ground when it is standing on all four paws?

.... m²

    ii) Calculate the pressure exerted by the polar bear on the ground.

.... N/m²

c) Snowshoes are shoes used for hiking through snow.

    i) Shiv puts on his snowshoes, which have a combined area of 0.4 m² in contact with the ground. How much pressure is Shiv exerting on the ground when he is wearing his snowshoes?

.... N/m²

    ii) Using the information in part a) and your answer to part c) i), why do you think snowshoes help people to walk through snow more easily?

....

....

....

d) In some old buildings with wooden floors, people wearing high-heeled shoes are asked to remove their shoes when they enter. Using your understanding of pressure, explain why.

....

....

....

....

Pressure Basics

5. Eloise is a cheerleader. In her routine, she has to stand on the shoulders of her partner, Harvey.

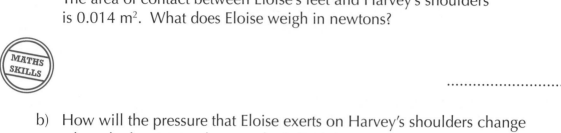

a) Eloise exerts a pressure of 40 000 N/m² on Harvey's shoulders. The area of contact between Eloise's feet and Harvey's shoulders is 0.014 m². What does Eloise weigh in newtons?

MATHS SKILLS

.... N

b) How will the pressure that Eloise exerts on Harvey's shoulders change when she has to stand on one leg? Explain your answer.

....

....

....

c) i) Eloise's coach decides that their routine needs to be more exciting and says Eloise should do a handstand on Harvey's shoulders. Eloise's hands have a greater area in contact with his shoulders than her feet did. Harvey says this will exert more pressure on him. Explain why Harvey is incorrect.

....

....

ii) Using your answer for Eloise's weight from part a), calculate the pressure exerted on Harvey's shoulders when Eloise does a handstand, if the area of contact between Eloise's hands and Harvey's shoulders is 0.016 m².

MATHS SKILLS

.... N/m²

d) In the show that Eloise and Harvey are performing in, there is a karate demonstration. The martial artist breaks a wooden block using his hand. Using your knowledge of pressure, explain why the block is more likely to be damaged when 'chopped' with the side of the hand than when it is hit with the palm of the hand.

....

....

....

....

Pressure in Fluids

1. Pressure in a fluid acts in all directions.

   a) What is meant by a fluid?

   ....

   b) What causes atmospheric pressure?

   ....

   c) Why does atmospheric pressure decrease as height above sea level increases?

   ....

   ....

2. An airship takes off from a field. Circle the correct words in these sentences to explain what is happening at different stages in the airship's flight.

   As the airship rises up, there is **more and more / less and less** atmosphere above it. The weight of the atmosphere pressing down on it **decreases / increases**, so the atmospheric pressure on the balloon **stays the same / decreases**.

   As the airship moves down, there is **more and more / less and less** atmosphere above it, so the weight of the atmosphere pressing down on it **decreases / increases**. The atmospheric pressure on the balloon **stays the same / increases**.

3. Henry has a bucket that has lots of holes of the same size in. He fills it with water and watches the water come out of the holes. The picture below shows what he sees.

   Henry's friend Liza notices that the water coming out of the holes closer to the bottom of the bucket travels further sideways. Why do you think this is?

   ....

   ....

   ....

   ....

Pressure in Fluids

4. Paul is a pilot. He takes a bag of crisps and a plastic bottle of water on a flight.

SCIENCE IN ACTION

a) During the flight, Paul notices the unopened crisp packet has expanded. Explain what has happened, in terms of pressure.

....

....

....

b) During his flight, he drinks the water and puts the lid back on the empty bottle. When he lands, the bottle has collapsed in on itself. Why do you think this happens?

....

....

....

5. The pressure in liquids can be used in hydraulic systems. The diagram below shows a hydraulic system with two pistons. A small force is applied to piston 1, which has a small area in contact with the liquid. Pressure is transmitted equally throughout the liquid. Piston 2 has a larger area in contact with the liquid, so a larger force is produced.

a) A force of 100 N is applied to piston 1, which has an area of 0.001 m² in contact with the liquid. Calculate the pressure at piston 1.

MATHS SKILLS

100 N

0.001 m²
Piston 1

0.004 m²
Piston 2

liquid

.... N/m²

b) The pressure at piston 2 is the same as at piston 1. Using your answer from part a), calculate the force acting on piston 2 if it has an area of 0.004 m² in contact with the liquid.

.... N

c) The system is reversed so that a force of 100 N is applied to piston 2 instead of piston 1. Without doing another calculation, explain why the force acting on piston 1 will be smaller than before.

....

....

....

Upthrust

1. Using the words below, complete this paragraph about pressure in liquids.
You may need to use some words more than once, and some words not at all.

| sink | increases | weight | decreases | upwards | downwards | upthrust | float |

Pressure in liquids .... with depth due to the .... of the

liquid above. Water pressure comes from all directions. When an object is in water,

the water pressure pushing upwards at the bottom of the object is greater than the water

pressure pushing .... at the top of the object. This causes an overall

.... force, which is called .... An object will sink until the

upthrust is equal to its ...., and then the object will ....

2. The diagram below shows the water pressure acting upwards
and downwards on a lemon that has been pushed underwater.

(MATHS SKILLS)

Water pressure 10.6 N

a) Calculate the size of the upthrust force on the lemon.

.... N

b) The lemon weighs 0.7 N. Will the lemon sink or float?

....

Water pressure 12 N

3. Mila submerges an inflated beach ball in a swimming pool.

a) Explain how water pressure causes upthrust on the beach ball.

....

....

....

b) Mila then deflates the beach ball and puts it in the water.
The deflated beach ball sinks. Why do you think this is?

....

....

Topic 1 — Pressure and Upthrust

Upthrust

4. Danny works on a submarine. The submarine weighs 72 000 000 N.

a) When the submarine is surfaced, the area of the submarine in contact with the water is 3200 m². Calculate the pressure exerted by the submarine on the water.

.... N/m²

b) The diagram below shows the submarine floating in water. Draw and label two arrows on the diagram showing the force created by the weight of the submarine and the upthrust force from the water.

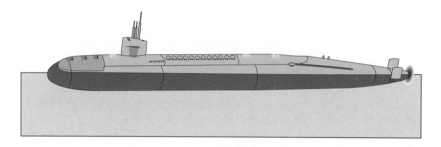

c) In the bottom of the submarine, there are ballast tanks that hold water. When necessary, water is allowed to flood into these tanks.

   i) Using your knowledge of weight and upthrust, explain how filling these tanks with water will affect the submarine.

   ....

   ....

   ....

   ....

   ii) Why do you think it is necessary that water can be pumped out of these tanks?

   ....

   ....

How did you do?

Don't let the pressure get to you — take your time to make sure you are happy that you:

☐ Can use the formula to calculate pressure acting on a surface.

☐ Understand that pressure in liquids increases with depth.

☐ Understand that atmospheric pressure decreases with height.

☐ Can explain the effect of upthrust on an object.

Topic 2 — Magnetism

Who doesn't love magnets? They're fun and can also be really useful to make things like compasses.

Learning Objectives

1. Know that the magnetic force is a non-contact force.
2. Know that magnetic fields have a north (N) and a south (S) pole.
3. Be able to predict how magnetic objects will behave in a magnetic field.
4. Know that magnetic materials and the Earth create magnetic fields.
5. Be able to draw field lines to show the strength and direction of a magnetic field.
6. Understand how the distance from a magnet affects the force felt by a magnetic object.

You may also hear the north and south poles of a magnet called north-seeking and south-seeking poles.

Before you Start

1. **Circle 'True' or 'False' to show if each sentence below is correct or not.**

   A magnet needs to be touching a paper clip to attract it.   **True / False**

   Magnets have two poles.   **True / False**

   Magnetic materials are repelled by a magnet.   **True / False**

   All metals are magnetic.   **True / False**

2. **Circle the things below that would be attracted to a magnet.**

   Steel Can   Candle   Iron Screw   A Rubber

3. **Write 'attract' or 'repel' next to each pair of magnets to show what will happen.**

   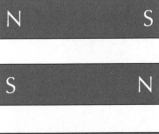

   N   S   N   S   ....

   S   N   N   S   ....

   N   S   S   N   ....

Magnetic Force

1. Teresa has a magnet and a small iron ball. She puts the magnet on a flat table.

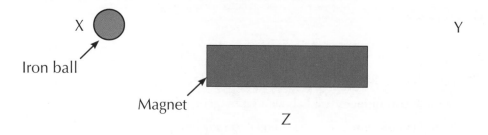

X

Iron ball

Magnet

Y

Z

a) Teresa places the small iron ball on the table at point X. It rolls towards the magnet. What force causes the ball to move towards the magnet?

....

b) Teresa places the ball at points Y and Z. The ball rolls towards the magnet each time. She says:

> My magnet must only have one pole because it always attracts the ball.

Explain how far you agree with Teresa.

....

....

c) Teresa rolls the ball slowly from point X towards point Y. What do you think will happen?

....

2. Jordan has three magnets that are labelled A, B and C. He puts the magnets in four different combinations. The results of combination 1 and 3 are shown on the right.

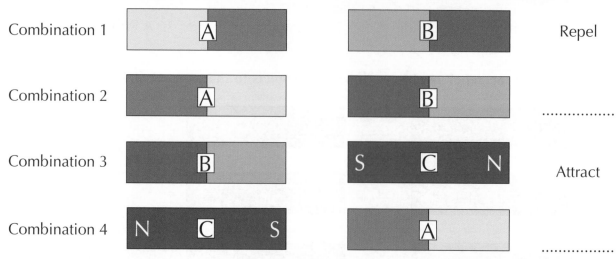

Combination 1 | A | B | Repel

Combination 2 | A | B | ....

Combination 3 | B | S C N | Attract

Combination 4 | N C S | A | ....

a) Predict and write in the result of combination 2.

b) In combination 4, label the north and south poles on magnet A and predict the outcome.

Magnetic Fields

1. Gemma has a magnet. The diagram below shows field lines around her magnet

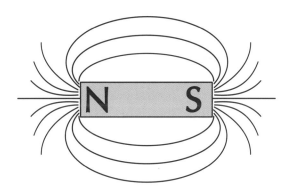

a) What is shown by the field lines?

....

b) Add arrows to the lines to show the direction of the field.

c) The lines are closer together near the poles of the magnet. What does this show?

....

....

d) Gemma has a trolley made from magnetic material. When she places the magnet 5 cm away from the trolley, as shown below, the trolley moves towards the magnet.

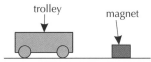

i) If the magnet is placed 20 cm away, the trolley does not move. Why doesn't the trolley move this time?

....

....

ii) Gemma rotates the magnet by 90°, as shown on the right. The distance of the trolley from the magnet is the same but this time the trolley moves towards the magnet. Why do you think that is?

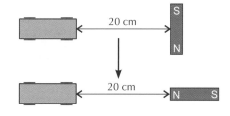

....

....

....

Magnetic Fields

2. Egan and Faye are hiking. Egan looks down at his magnetic compass.

SCIENCE IN ACTION

a) What Egan sees is shown on the right. Which direction is Egan facing?

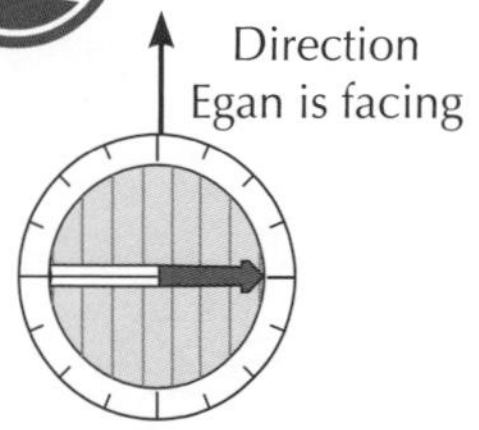

....

Direction Egan is facing

b) Egan turns through 90°. The arrow on the compass is still pointing in the same direction, as shown on the right. Explain why.

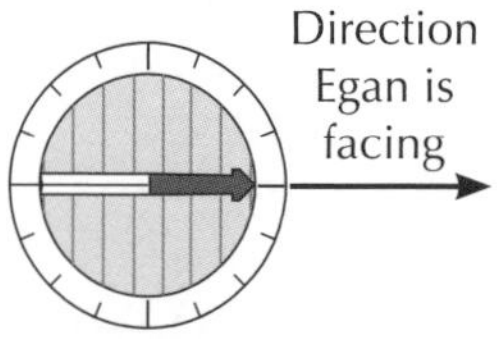

....

....

....

Direction Egan is facing

c) Faye puts her magnetic compass next to Egan's. This causes the needle in Egan's compass to point in a different direction. Explain why.

....

....

3. The diagrams below show the magnetic field at the north and south pole of a magnet.

Where's all the grass?

N

S

Diagram A

Diagram B

N

S

N

N

a) On diagram A, draw what the field lines would look like if the north and south poles of two magnets were placed close together.

b) On diagram B, draw what the field lines would look like if the north poles of two magnets were placed close together.

How did you do?

That's all for this magnets topic — hopefully you weren't repelled by these questions. Make sure you:

☐ Know that the magnetic force is non-contact.

☐ Can draw field lines.

☐ Can predict how magnetic objects will behave in a magnetic field.

☐ Understand how the strength of a magnetic field changes with distance.

Topic 3 — Electromagnets

This topic is all about magnets that can be turned on and off — electromagnets.

Learning Objectives

1. Know that an electric current creates a magnetic field.
2. Know that the strength of the magnetic field of an electromagnet decreases with distance.
3. Understand the factors that affect the strength of a magnetic field around an electromagnet.
4. Be able to evaluate the use of electromagnets in devices.

Before you Start

1. **Circle the objects that create a magnetic field.**

2. **Are these statements about magnetic fields true or false? Tick the correct box.**

	True	False
Magnetic field lines point from a magnet's south pole to its north pole.	☐	☐
The strength of a magnetic field around a magnet is the same everywhere.	☐	☐
If the strength of a magnetic field is increased, the force on a magnetic object in the field increases.	☐	☐

3. **The diagram below shows a permanent magnet. Draw field lines to show the magnetic field produced by the magnet.**

N   S

Magnetic Effect of a Current

1. A diagram of the magnetic field around an electromagnet is shown below.

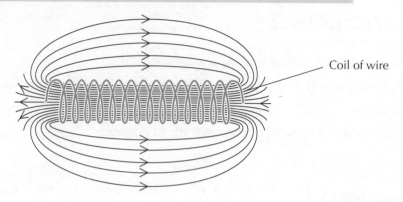

Coil of wire

    a) Label the north and south pole of the electromagnet.

    b) What is the coil of wire also known as?

       ....

    c) What would happen if the north pole of a permanent magnet was placed near the north pole of the electromagnet?

       ....

2. A student is setting up a circuit (shown right) in her classroom. A magnetic compass has been left on the bench by another student. The student notices that when she closes the switch on the circuit the compass needle moves.

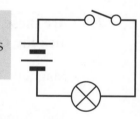

    a) Why does the compass needle move when the switch is closed?

       ....

       ....

       ....

    b) Explain what you think will happen to the compass when the student opens the switch.

       ....

       ....

       ....

    c) The student moves the compass further away from the circuit. This time when she closes the switch the compass needle does not move. Why is this?

       ....

       ....

Using Electromagnets

1. Electromagnets and permanent magnets have different uses.

    a) Draw lines between the boxes to show which type of magnet is most suitable for which task.

Electromagnet	For a clasp to keep a wallet closed.
	Picking up and dropping steel cans.
Permanent magnet	Pinning a note to your fridge.
	Lifting a maglev train off the tracks.

    b) Electromagnets are used to pick up cars in scrapyards.
        Give one reason why electromagnets are better than permanent magnets for this job.

        ....

        ....

2. Ronald is building an electromagnet that he wants to use for picking up and dropping magnetic objects. He has a cell and a coil of wire, as shown below.

    a) Ronald also plans to place a nail in the centre of the coil.
        Why do you think Ronald wants to do this?

        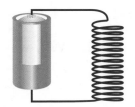

        ....

        ....

    Ronald tests three nails, each made of a different material. He tries to pick up each nail with a magnet, and then tries to use that nail to pick up some iron filings. His results are shown in the table below.

Nail	Picked up by magnet	Picked up iron filings
Material 1	✗	✗
Material 2	✓	✓
Material 3	✓	✗

    b) i) Why isn't a nail made from material 1 suitable for Ronald's electromagnet?

        ....

        ....

Using Electromagnets

ii) Why isn't a nail made from material 2 suitable for Ronald's electromagnet?

....

....

3. Aziz is investigating how the number of coils affects the strength of an **PRACTICAL** electromagnet. He links paper clips together into chains of different lengths. Aziz tests the strength of the magnet by counting the number of paper clips in the longest chain the magnet can hold. His set-up and results are shown below.

Number of coils	Number of paper clips in longest chain			
	Attempt 1	Attempt 2	Attempt 3	Mean
10	3	3	3	....
20	8	7	9	....
30	14	12	13	....
40	17	17	20	....

a) Calculate and fill in the mean column of the table.

MATHS SKILLS

b) Why was the electromagnet able to hold more paper clips when there were more coils?

....

....

....

c) Aziz looks at his results. He says:

> To pick up an extra paper clip you need to add 2 coils to the magnet.

Do you agree with Aziz? Explain your answer.

....

....

....

d) Other than increasing the number of coils, what could Aziz do to hold more paper clips with the electromagnet?

....

Using Electromagnets

4. Amina builds an electric motor to power a fan.

The diagram shows Amina's fan. Why does the fan turn when the switch is closed?

....

....

....

....

permanent magnets

fan

cell

coil

5. A diagram of an electric bell is shown on the right.

a) When the switch is first closed the iron arm moves towards the electromagnet. Why is this?

....

....

....

....

....

bell striker

iron arm

contacts

bell

electromagnet

switch

spring

cell

SCIENCE IN ACTION

b) Why does the electromagnet turn off as the iron arm moves towards it?

....

c) The iron arm springs back when the electromagnet is off.
Explain why this causes the bell to ring while the switch is closed.

....

....

....

How did you do?

That was a lot of electromagnet questions but hopefully they're now your specialist field. You should:

☐ Know that current creates a magnetic field.

☐ Know the magnetic field is weaker further from an electromagnet.

☐ Know how to make an electromagnet stronger.

☐ Be able to evaluate the use of electromagnets.

 ☐   ☐   ☐

Topic 4 — Work

No, not the "fun" work where you get paid. The physics kind of work, where... Well, we'll get to that.

Learning Objectives

1. Know that work done is the energy transferred when a force moves an object over a given distance.
2. Know how to use the equation: work done (J) = force (N) × distance moved (m).
3. Know that machines (levers, pulleys and wheels) reduce the force needed to move an object.
4. Know how turning forces and moments are used in levers.

Before you Start

1. The diagram below shows a see-saw.

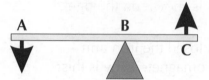

   Which of the letters (A-C) labels the pivot of the see-saw?

   ☐ A   ☐ B   ☐ C

2. Likhita has bought a tin of fuchsia pink paint to repaint her bedroom with.
   Which one of the following ways do you think would make it easiest to open the tin?
   Tick the box next to the correct answer.

   ☐ using her hands   ☐ using a pulley   ☐ using a screwdriver

3. Below are some measurements and some units.
   Draw lines to connect the measurements to the correct units.

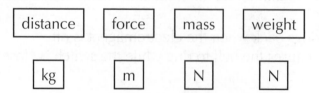

4. The diagram below shows a group of people pulling a rock. The arrow shows the
   direction of the force that the people are applying to the rock. Add an arrow to show
   the direction of the opposing force that the rock is applying to the people.

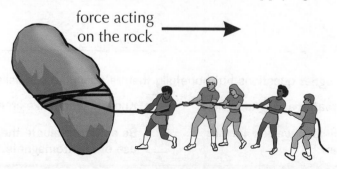

force acting
on the rock

Work Done and Energy Transfer

1. The diagram below shows an employee in a factory pushing a box along the floor.

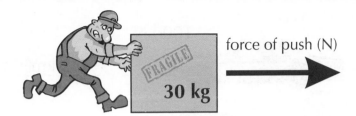

force of push (N)

30 kg

a) The employee is doing work on the box. What is meant by the term 'work done'?

....

....

b) The employee adds a second box on top of the first box. This means the employee has to use more force to push the boxes. Do you think that adding the second box will affect the amount of work needed to move the boxes? Explain your answer.

....

....

....

c) The employee now has to push the same boxes a greater distance. How will this affect the amount of work needed? Explain your answer.

....

....

....

2. Complete the table below by filling in the columns for total displacement and total distance for each of the three journeys described. Each journey takes place on flat ground.

Journey	Total displacement (m)	Total distance (m)
Jolene walks 20 m from her house to her friend's house for a sleepover.		
A runner runs one lap round a 300 m running track.		
A cyclist cycles 750 m to the shops and then cycles back.		

Work Done and Energy Transfer

3. Look at the diagrams below and state which mode of transport has the most work done to move it the distance shown. Show your working.

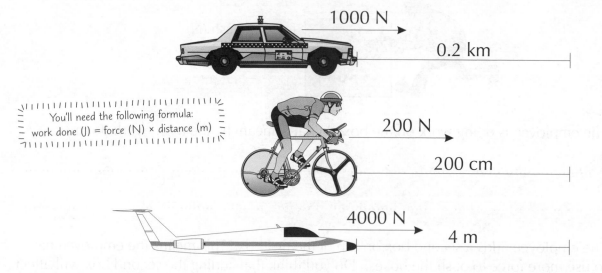

1000 N

0.2 km

You'll need the following formula:
work done (J) = force (N) × distance (m)

200 N

200 cm

4000 N

4 m

....

4. Little Jimmy used 4 N of force, and did 12 J of work, to move a cart. Calculate how far Little Jimmy moved the cart. Show your working.

.... m

5. The diagram shows an electric motor being used to raise a load. The motor rotates, causing the rubber band to move. This causes the wheel to turn. A shaft on the wheel has the load attached to it by a string. As the wheel turns, the shaft turns and raises the load.

Explain how the electric motor
is doing work to raise the load.

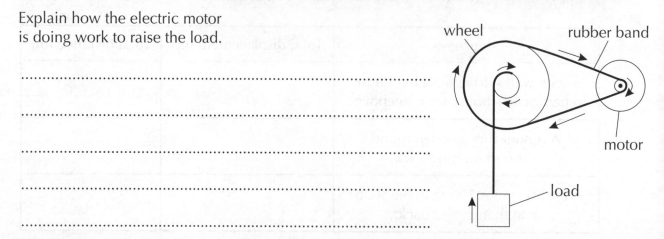

wheel   rubber band

motor

load

....

....

....

....

Levers, Pulleys and Wheels

1. Describe what is meant by the following terms.

turning force: ....

....

moment: ....

....

2. Ryan and his friend Joe are waiting in the airport to go on holiday together. Ryan's suitcase has wheels but the wheels on Joe's suitcase have broken off. Both suitcases have the same mass.

Why will the wheels make Ryan's suitcase easier to pull along the floor than Joe's suitcase?

....

....

....

3. Cleo the dog is after some tasty treats. The diagram below shows her using a lever to get a box off a shelf.

DO NOT TOUCH
Precious
Archaeological
Finds

a) Draw a label on the diagram to show where the pivot is.

b) In which direction will the box first move when Cleo applies a downward force on the lever?

....

Levers, Pulleys and Wheels

c) Complete the sentences below by circling the correct word.

The downward force on the lever that Cleo applies is the **input / output** force.

The force that acts on the box after Cleo applies the force is the **input / output** force.

Spot the cat says to Cleo:

> If you push down closer to the pivot, you'll find it easier to move the box because you're applying the force closer to the box.

d) Do you think that Spot is correct? Explain your answer.

....

....

....

....

4. Paula has been called out to fix a leaking toilet. Paula needs to tighten up a nut on a pipe. She has two spanners in her toolbox that she could use. The spanners are shown below.

Which spanner do you think Paula would find it easier to use to turn the nut? Explain your answer.

SCIENCE IN ACTION

Ⓐ Ⓑ

....

....

....

....

....

5. Pulleys are machines that can be used to lift masses more easily. The mass is lifted by pulling down on a rope.

a) In the simplest type of pulley, the input and output forces are equal. Some pulleys reduce the input force needed, but to get the same output force to lift the same mass the same distance, you have to pull the rope further. Explain why.

....

....

....

Topic 4 — Work

Levers, Pulleys and Wheels

The diagram shows three different pulleys, each with a different number of wheels.
All three pulleys have the same sized mass attached. Assume the wheels have no mass.

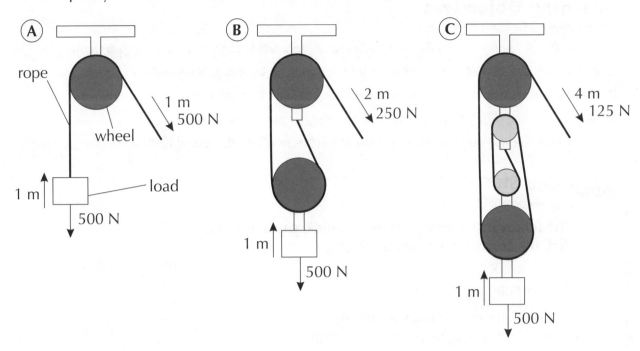

After looking at the three pulleys, Susannah says:

> I think that pulley B is the most suitable pulley to use to lift the load.

b) Explain **one** reason why:

    i) Pulley A might **not** be the most suitable pulley to use to lift the load.

      ....

      ....

    ii) Pulley C might **not** be the most suitable pulley to use to lift the load.

      ....

      ....

How did you do?

That's enough work done for one day. Wait a moment before you lever the cover of the book closed and pull-ey on your PJs, and tick off the learning objectives below. By now you wheel-y should:

- ☐ Know that work is done when a force moves an object.
- ☐ Understand that machines reduce the force needed to move an object.
- ☐ Understand the equation for work done.
- ☐ Know how turning forces are used in levers.

  😊☐

Topic 4 — Work

Topic 5 — Thermal Energy

These next few pages have high thermal energy (they're hot stuff) — I'm excited to get stuck in...

Learning Objectives

1. Know that a temperature difference between objects will lead to thermal energy transfer.
2. Know that the thermal energy of an object depends on its mass, temperature and material.
3. Understand how an object's temperature changes over time when it's heated or cooled.
4. Understand the different ways that thermal energy can be transferred.
5. Know how thermal conductors and thermal insulators affect the speed of thermal energy transfer.

Before you Start

1. **The following statements refer to solids, gases or both.
Tick the correct box to show which.**

	solids	gases	both
The particles are fixed in position.	☐	☐	☐
The particles of a substance have more energy in this state than when it's a liquid.	☐	☐	☐
Heating causes the particles to vibrate or move more.	☐	☐	☐

2. **Jocinta makes two cups of hot tea — one in a metal cup and one in a cardboard cup.**

   a) Which cup will feel hotter?

   ☐ The metal cup ☐ The cardboard cup ☐ They'll both feel the same

   b) Will the teas get hotter or colder over time?

   ....

   c) When Jocinta holds her hand over one of the cups of tea, her hand feels warmer.
   Tick the box next to the statement you think is correctly describing why.

   Heat particles from the tea are moving to Jocinta's hand. ☐

   The tea is heating up the air over the cup. ☐

   The cold from the air moves into the tea, so the air feels warmer. ☐

3. **Describe what a particle in a solid is doing when it is vibrating.**

   ....

Thermal Energy and Temperature

1. Below are several statements about temperature. Tick one of the boxes for each statement depending on whether you think it's true or false.

True   False

'Temperature' and 'heat' are the same thing. ☐ ☐

A fall in temperature happens because thermal energy moves out of an object. ☐ ☐

The temperature of an object depends on how much energy its particles have. ☐ ☐

2. The diagram below shows two blocks that are touching. They are made from identical material but one is bigger. One block has been heated and one block has been chilled.

a) In which direction will the transfer of thermal energy occur?

heated block   chilled block

....

....

b) i) Describe what will happen to the temperature difference between the two blocks over time.

....

....

....

ii) When the two blocks are in thermal equilibrium, will they have the same thermal energy as each other? Explain your answer.

....

....

....

c) The graph shows how the temperature of one of the blocks changes over time.

PRACTICAL

i) Add a second line to the graph to show the change in temperature of the other block. The initial temperature of the other block is marked on the axis with an X.

ii) Put a cross on the graph where you think thermal equilibrium between the blocks occurred.

Temperature (°C)

X

Time (mins)

Topic 5 — Thermal Energy

Thermal Energy Transfers

1. Draw a line between each method of transferring
    thermal energy and the description which fits it best.

| convection | | Happens when particles collide with one another. |

| conduction | | Occurs in fluids. |

| radiation | | Doesn't rely on the movement of particles. |

2. The diagram shows an example of a lake cooling system. **SCIENCE IN ACTION**

1. Water flows through a pipe
   in the walls of the house.
   Thermal energy from the
   house transfers into the
   pipe by conduction and then
   to the water in the pipe.

2. The pipe passes through a cool
   lake and as water flows through
   this section of pipe, it transfers
   thermal energy to the lake.

3. The cooled water in the pipe
   flows back into the house.

a) i) Below are some features of the pipe. Place a tick in the box next to each feature the
        pipe should have so that it transfers the most thermal energy to the water in the lake.

☐ insulating   ☐ conducting

☐ made from thin metal   ☐ made from thick metal

ii) Explain your answer to question a) i).

....

....

....

....

b) Draw an arrow on the diagram to show the convection current that will form in the lake.

c) Describe one similarity and one difference between conduction and convection.

similarity: ....

....

difference: ....

....

Thermal Energy Transfers

3. The diagram shows a radiator heating the air in a room.

radiator

hot air

a) Most radiators are made of metal, which is a thermal conductor. What is meant by the term 'thermal conductor'?

....

....

b) Despite their name, radiators mostly work by conduction. Describe how the radiator has heated the hot air.

....

....

c) Describe the convection current that forms in the air in the room.

....

....

....

d) A person puts their hand against the radiator. With reference to particles, describe how thermal energy is transferred from the radiator to the person's hand.

....

....

....

....

4. Two equally sized potatoes are cooking in the oven. One of the potatoes has a metal skewer pushed into it.

SCIENCE IN ACTION

With reference to the transfer of thermal energy, explain which potato will cook faster.

....

....

....

....

....

Topic 5 — Thermal Energy

Reducing Thermal Energy Transfer

1. Air is a poor conductor of thermal energy. An outdoor jacket helps to keep the wearer warm by using fake fur to trap pockets of air against the wearer and stop the air moving.

Using the information provided, give two ways that you think trapping air against the wearer helps to insulate the wearer against the cold.

....

....

....

....

....

2. The diagram shows the inside of a vacuum flask.

SCIENCE IN ACTION

stopper

thin, shiny outer edge

vacuum between edges

thin, shiny inner edge

liquid

The shiny edges reflect waves. The vacuum means that there's no air between the edges.

a) Explain how the features of the vacuum flask help to reduce the transfer of thermal energy by the following methods:

convection: ....

....

conduction: ....

....

radiation: ....

....

Reducing Thermal Energy Transfer

b) Three friends have the same make of vacuum flask. They say the following things:

> Suzie: I put soup in my vacuum flask and it stays warm until I eat it at lunchtime.

> Leeroy: I put apple juice in my vacuum flask and it stays cool all morning.

> Jamal: The same vacuum flask can't keep things hot and cold. It must only be able to do one.

Do you agree with Jamal? Explain your answer.

....

....

....

....

3. Damien receives the flyer below from a window glazing company.

SCIENCE IN ACTION

metal spacer

glass panes

trapped air

metal spacer

Gumption Glazers Ltd.

Our double-glazed windows use two glass panes with air trapped between them to insulate your home. The air insulates the glass against the cold as it doesn't conduct heat very well.

We use metal spacers pressed against both panes of glass to keep them the perfect distance apart.

Prevents **any** heat escaping through your windows.

Use the information provided in the flyer to assess the claim made at the bottom.

....

....

....

....

....

How did you do?

Make sure you've transferred everything from these pages into your brain. By now you should:

☐ Know what thermal energy is and understand when thermal energy is transferred.

☐ Understand the ways thermal energy is transferred.

☐ Know how temperature changes with time during heating and cooling.

☐ Know how conductors and insulators affect the speed of thermal energy transfer.

 ☐   ☐   ☐

Topic 6 — Wave Properties

This topic is all about waves — the different kinds, how they act and how they interact. Just smile and wave.

Learning Objectives

1. Know the properties of transverse and longitudinal waves.
2. Understand the model of a transverse wave.
3. Know the similarities and differences between sound waves and light waves.
4. Be able to explain how a wave model shows reflection, absorption and transmission.
5. Understand what happens when two waves meet.

Before you Start

1. **Circle 'True' or 'False' to show if each sentence below is correct or not.**

All the particles making up a sound wave always travel at the same speed as the sound wave.	True / False
Sound is an example of a pressure wave.	True / False
Sound waves transfer energy and particles.	True / False
Sound waves are longitudinal.	True / False

2. **Complete the diagram below to show light from the torch being reflected by the mirror.**

3. **Ellen shouts in the mountains and hears her voice repeated back to her. Explain what is happening to cause this effect.**

   ....

   ....

4. **What does the 'frequency of a wave' mean?**

   ....

   ....

Transverse and Longitudinal Waves

1. Put ticks in the boxes to show which statements are true for transverse and longitudinal waves.

	Transverse Wave	**Longitudinal Wave**
a) Particles in the wave move perpendicular to the movement of the wave.	☐	☐
b) These waves transfer energy.	☐	☐
c) These waves contain areas of low and high pressure.	☐	☐
d) These waves have an amplitude.	☐	☐
e) These waves can be reflected.	☐	☐
f) All kinds of these waves need a medium to travel through.	☐	☐

2. The diagram below shows a model of a wave.

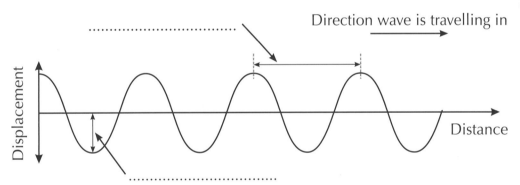

Direction wave is travelling in

Displacement

Distance

a) i) Fill in the labels on the diagram.

   ii) Draw an arrow on the diagram to show the direction that energy is being transferred in by the wave.

b) i) Does the diagram above show a transverse or longitudinal wave?

   ....

   ii) Give an example of a wave of this kind.

   ....

c) Draw a wave on the axes below with a greater frequency than the wave above.

Displacement

Distance

Topic 6 — Wave Properties

Transverse and Longitudinal Waves

3. Use the words given in the box to complete the sentences below comparing light waves and sound waves. You won't need to use all the words in the box.

> energy   opposite   both   longitudinal
> air   sound   transverse   light   perpendicular

Light and sound are both examples of waves. Light is a .... wave, which

means that the direction of the vibration of the waves is .... to the direction

the wave is travelling in. Sound is a .... wave, which means that the

direction of the vibration of the wave is parallel to the direction the wave is travelling in.

.... waves need a medium to travel through, such as ....

Both waves transfer ....

4. The diagram below shows a transverse water wave in the sea hitting a sea wall.

 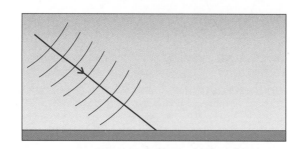

a) i) What will happen to the water waves when they hit the wall?

....

ii) Complete the diagram to show this.

b) Describe how the water particles in the wave will be moving.

....

....

....

Wave Properties

1. A rope is tied to a metal ring on a wall and the other end is held 3 metres way. Manoj flicks the rope up to create a wave which travels along the rope.

a) What kind of wave is travelling along the rope, transverse or longitudinal?

....

Manoj flicks the rope again, this time harder, to see what effect this has on the wave. Both waves have the same wavelength.

b) What is the difference between the two waves that travelled along the rope?

....

c) Compare the speed of the second wave Manoj produced with the first.

....

d) Manoj wants to investigate the effect of flicking the rope harder. Give two factors he should keep the same to make the test fair.

PRACTICAL

....

....

e) What do you think will happen to the wave when it reaches the wall?

....

2. When two waves meet they can combine.

a) The diagram below shows two water waves travelling towards each other. Draw diagrams in the boxes below to show what happens when the waves meet and what happens after the waves have met.

Before the waves meet | As the waves meet | After the waves meet

b) What term is used to describe what happens when two waves meet like in part a?

....

Topic 6 — Wave Properties

Wave Properties

3. Transverse waves can be modelled by surface ripples on water.

   a) Explain how each wave property is shown by the ripples in the photo on the right:

   i) Transmission: ....

   ....

   ii) Absorption: ....

   ....

Two stones are thrown into a pond. They create waves which ripple outwards from where they entered the water. The diagram shows crosses where the stones hit the water. The circles show the crests of the waves. The crests of both waves are the same height.

   b) Describe what happens at the points where two crests meet.

   ....

   ....

   c) On the diagram, draw a spot at a point where the trough of the waves will be lowest.

   d) Describe what will happen to the waves at point A.

   ....

   ....

The diagram below shows the ripples from a stone thrown into the pond close to a wall. The cross shows where the stone hit the water and the grey lines show the crests of the waves caused by the stone.

   e) What do you think the blue lines show?

   ....

How did you do?

It's time to wave goodbye to waves and their properties for now, but not before making sure you:

☐ Can compare the similarities and differences between transverse and longitudinal waves.

☐ Understand the model of a transverse wave.

☐ Can compare sound waves and light waves.

☐ Can explain how a wave model can show reflection, absorption, transmission.

☐ Know what happens when two waves meet.

Topic 7 — Elements

Time to get down to the meat and potatoes of what makes everything up (but don't start doing that here).

Learning Objectives

1. Know what atoms and elements are.
2. Understand the structure of the periodic table.
3. Recognise and describe patterns in chemical and physical properties within the periodic table.

Before you Start

1. **Sort the properties by whether they are more likely to belong to a metal or a non-metal.**

low density   ductile

magnetic   shiny   dull

low melting point

insulator of heat   brittle

electrical conductor

Metal	Non-metal

2. **Which of these sentences are true and which are false?**

	True	False
A pure substance is a single type of material with nothing mixed in.	☐	☐
An atom is a type of particle.	☐	☐
All gases are highly reactive, because their particles move very quickly.	☐	☐
All metals have the same chemical properties.	☐	☐

3. **Circle the things you think you would find in the periodic table.**

aluminium   oxygen   wood

plastic   bromine

copper   fire   glass   Billy the goat

Atoms and Elements

1. Put a tick under any particle diagram that could represent an element.

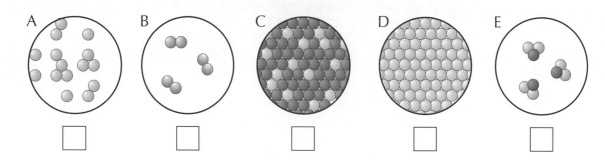

A B C D E

☐ ☐ ☐ ☐ ☐

2. Complete this paragraph using words from the word bank. You won't need all of them.

| few | largest | see | hottest | different | taste | smallest | measure | four |

Atoms are the .... particles of an element that can exist. It took a long time for atoms to be discovered, because you can't .... them directly. The first modern theory about atoms stated that all matter is made up of atoms and that there are .... types of atom.

3. True or False:

	True	False
a) Elements can only contain one type of atom.	☐	☐
b) Elements are made when atoms are combined.	☐	☐
c) Elements are always solid at room temperature.	☐	☐
d) There are over 100 elements.	☐	☐
e) Elements all tend to have the same chemical properties.	☐	☐

4. Hiroki has a brass statue. Brass is made from copper and zinc.

Hiroki says, "brass is an element because it doesn't contain any impurities".
Is Hiroki right? Explain your reasoning.

....

....

....

Atoms and Elements

5. Symbols can be used to represent elements.

Use the periodic table at the back of the book to help you with this question and the rest of the topic.

a) Draw arrows to match each element to its symbol.

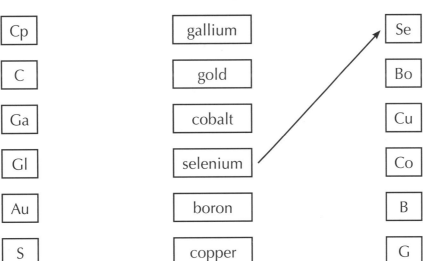

Cp		gallium		Se
C		gold		Bo
Ga		cobalt		Cu
Gl		selenium		Co
Au		boron		B
S		copper		G

b) What are the symbols for these elements?

i) nitrogen ....

ii) bromine ....

iii) sodium ....

c) Water has the symbol H_2O. Why is water not an element?

....

....

d) Tick the boxes below the elements in these equations.

i) iron oxide + carbon → iron + carbon dioxide

$2Fe_2O_3$ + $3C$ → $4Fe$ + $3CO_2$

☐ ☐ ☐ ☐

ii) magnesium + hydrochloric acid → magnesium chloride + hydrogen

Mg + $2HCl$ → $MgCl_2$ + H_2

☐ ☐ ☐ ☐

Topic 7 — Elements

The Periodic Table

1. Circle the correct options in this paragraph about the periodic table.

An early periodic table was put together by a scientist called Mendeleev,
who put elements with similar properties in the same **rows / columns** .
Elements that are close together in the table tend to have similar properties.
For example, all the non-metal elements are found on the **right / left** of the table.
The columns of the table are called **periods / groups** .
The elements in the first column are all very **reactive / unreactive** .

2. Look at the periodic table below. It shows the positions and symbols of some elements.

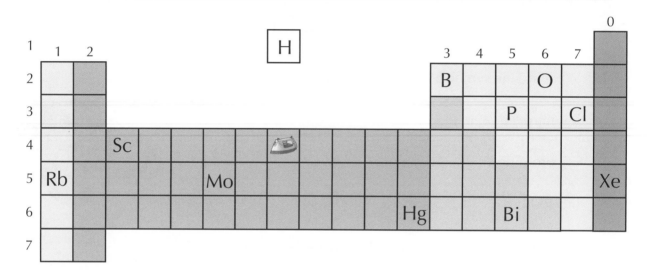

a) Which of the elements shown in the table above are non-metals?
Write down their symbols.

....

b) Write the symbol of an element shown in this table that:

i) is in period 5 ....

ii) is a noble gas ....

iii) is in group 6 ....

iv) is a halogen ....

v) will react vigorously with water ....

The Periodic Table

3. A scientist is studying the physical properties of Group 1 elements.

a) What is another name for the elements in Group 1? ....

b) The size of the atoms increases down Group 1.
Which Group 1 element has the smallest atoms? ....

The scientist measures the melting points and boiling points of the elements in Group 1.
Some of her results are shown in the table.

c) Describe the trend in melting point.

....

....

....

Element	Melting Point (°C)
lithium	180.5
sodium	97.7
potassium	63.4
rubidium	39.3
caesium	?

d) Estimate the melting point of caesium.

.... °C

e) How do you think the boiling point will change down Group 1?

....

4. Maya is looking at the reactions of the Group 2 elements with hydrochloric acid.

a) Calcium and barium are both in Group 2. Calcium reacts vigorously with
hydrochloric acid to produce calcium chloride and hydrogen gas.
What do you think the reaction of barium with hydrochloric acid will be like?
Explain your answer.

....

....

....

b) How do you think magnesium and hydrochloric acid will react? Explain your answer.

....

....

....

The Periodic Table

5. The densities of some elements are shown in the graph.

> Use the periodic table at the back of the book to help you with this question.

a) Predict the density of rhodium, Rh.

.... g/cm³

b) Explain why you chose that value.

....

....

....

....

....

....

6. Jo carries out several displacement reactions using halogens and records her results.

Reactants	Reaction Result
chlorine + bromine salt solution	chlorine displaces bromine
iodine + chlorine salt solution	no reaction
bromine + iodine salt solution	bromine displaces iodine

a) In the halogens, chlorine is above bromine and bromine is above iodine. Jo says "the halogens become less reactive down the group". Is she right?

☐ yes   ☐ no

How do Jo's results provide evidence for this?

....

....

....

b) What do you think would happen if astatine was added to a bromine salt solution? Explain your answer.

....

....

....

The Periodic Table

7. False teeth can be used to replace missing teeth. A scientist wants to make a set of false teeth.

The scientist has several elements, shown below, that he could make the teeth from.

silver			iron		lithium	

chlorine   bromine   krypton

a) Circle the element you think is most suitable for making the teeth.

b) Using the periodic table and your own knowledge, give a reason why each of the other elements is unsuitable for making the teeth.

....

....

....

....

....

....

8. A researcher has an unidentifed element, **J**, which has a boiling point of $-108\,°C$. She suspects **J** is either chlorine, neon or xenon.

Element	Boiling Point (°C)
F	−188
Cl	?
I	184
Ne	?
Kr	−153
Xe	?
Rn	−62

a) Using the table on the right and what you know about the elements and trends in the periodic table, which of the elements below is definitely not element **J**? Tick one box.

☐ chlorine   ☐ neon   ☐ xenon

b) The researcher then discovers that element **J** does not react with acids or with a solution of an iodine salt. What element is **J**? Explain your answer.

....

....

How did you do?

Phew, those questions can be periodically puzzling. Hopefully by now you're in your element when it comes to the periodic table. By now you should be able to smugly tick off these objectives:

☐ Know your atoms from your elements.   ☐ Recognise patterns within the periodic table.

☐ Know how the periodic table is arranged.   ☐ Use trends to predict properties of elements.

            Topic 7 — Elements

Topic 8 — Compounds

Congratulations, you've mastered elements. There's only one thing to do now — mash some together.

Learning Objectives

1. Know what compounds and molecules are.
2. Identify a substance from particle diagrams, as atoms or molecules, or as an element, mixture or compound.
3. Be able to name simple compounds from their chemical formulae.
4. Use chemical formulae to represent elements and compounds.
5. Identify a substance as an element or compound from a chemical reaction.
6. Describe properties of ceramics, polymers and composites.

Before you Start

Have a quick look at the periodic table at the back if you need to.

1. **Which of the following represent elements? Circle the correct answers.**

   Sc   Br   CO H_2O KF

   CO_2 Cl_2 HCl   Co O_3

2. **Draw lines to match the word to its description.**

   | Atom |

   | Element |

   | Mixture |

   Something made up of two or more substances that aren't chemically joined up.

   A very small particle.

   A substance that contains only one type of atom.

3. **Tick the correct box to sort the substances below into elements or mixtures.**

Substance	Element	Mixture
carbon		
air		
seawater		
paint		
titanium		

Molecules and Compounds

1. Are the following sentences true or false? Tick the correct box.

True   False

a) Compounds are made up of different types of atom. ☐ ☐

b) Compounds naturally turn back into elements over time. ☐ ☐

c) Molecules contain chemical bonds. ☐ ☐

d) You can find some compounds in the periodic table. ☐ ☐

e) Compounds can be pure substances. ☐ ☐

f) Molecules must contain at least two different types of atom. ☐ ☐

2. Look at the particle diagrams, **A-F**, shown on the right.

A   B

a) Which two diagrams show a mixture?

....

b) Which of the remaining diagrams show a compound?

....

C   D

c) How many diagrams show a pure substance?

....

d) Which diagrams contain only one type of molecule (and nothing else)?

....

E   F

e) Which diagram could represent a mixture of nitrogen (N_2) and carbon monoxide (CO)?

....

Explain your choice.

....

....

....

....

Molecules and Compounds

3. Fiona has two beakers. One beaker contains water and the other contains hydrochloric acid.
   She adds some small pieces of iron metal to each beaker and stirs the contents.

   a) A reaction occurs between the acid and the iron.
      Complete the word equation for this reaction.

      PRACTICAL

      iron + hydrochloric acid → .... chloride + ...

   b) Give one safety precaution that Fiona should have taken before carrying out this reaction.

      ....

   c) Fiona wants to retrieve the iron from the beakers.

      i) She sets up the apparatus
         shown on the right.
         Label the apparatus.

         ....

         ....

         ....

      ii) Iron does not dissolve in water. How can Fiona use the apparatus
          above to obtain iron from the beaker containing water?

          ....

          ....

          ....

      iii) Iron chloride dissolves in water. Why can't Fiona use the method shown in the
           diagram above to obtain iron from the beaker containing hydrochloric acid?

           ....

           ....

           ....

   d) Fiona also has a sample of iron iodide, FeI_2. She wants to split this up into iron and
      iodine. Iron has a much higher melting point than iodine, so Fiona intends to heat the
      sample until the iodine has melted off, then collect the iron. Which sentence is correct?

      ☐ Fiona's method will work because iron iodide is a mixture.

      ☐ Fiona's method won't work because the iron iodide will
         have a different melting point to iron and iodine.

      ☐ Fiona's method won't work because she won't be able
         to get the sample hot enough to melt iodine.

Molecules and Compounds

4. Compounds have both a written name and a chemical formula.

a) How many oxygen atoms are there in one molecule of H_2O? ....

b) What is the name of $MgSO_4$?

☐ magnesium hydroxide   ☐ magnesium sulfoxide

☐ magnesium sulfate   ☐ magnesium sulfide

c) Predict the chemical formula of calcium sulfate. ....

d) Fill in the table to show the elements in a molecule of $SOBr_2$. How many atoms of each element are there?

Name of Element	Number of Atoms

5. Nitrogen trichloride is an explosive substance that can be made by treating ammonium chloride (a salt) with chlorine. It is made up of small molecules.

a) What is a molecule?

....

....

b) What do you think the formula of nitrogen trichloride is? ....

c) Vincent is investigating the properties of nitrogen trichloride. He says:

> Nitrogen trichloride contains nitrogen. Nitrogen is a gas at room temperature, therefore nitrogen trichloride will be a gas at room temperature as well.

Do you agree with Vincent? Explain your answer.

....

....

....

....

Molecules and Compounds

6. When oxygen and nitrogen react at high temperatures, they can produce nitrogen dioxide as the only product.

a) From this information, how do you know that nitrogen dioxide is a compound?

....

....

b) The boiling point of nitrogen dioxide is 21 °C.
Anuja sketches particle diagrams for nitrogen dioxide at two different temperatures.

−10 °C   5 °C

Key

nitrogen dioxide

i) Estimate the melting point of nitrogen dioxide. ....°C

ii) Sketch a particle diagram for nitrogen dioxide at 45 °C.

7. Chloroform, $CHCl_3$, is a sweet smelling liquid that can be used as a solvent.

a) Name all the elements that make up chloroform.

....

b) i) Give one property of chloroform that makes it suitable for use as a solvent.

....

ii) Why would a mixture of the same elements not make a suitable solvent?

....

....

Molecules and Compounds

8. Hypochlorites, such as sodium hypochlorite and lithium hypochlorite, can be added to swimming pools to kill germs. Sodium hypochlorite (NaClO) can decompose into sodium chloride (NaCl) and oxygen (O_2).

Grace and Erica are talking about the products of this reaction.

> Grace: O_2 contains two oxygen atoms that are bonded together, so it must be a compound.

> Erica: O_2 is pure because it contains only one element. NaCl can't be pure because it contains two different elements.

a) i) Which of them is right?

☐ just Grace   ☐ both Grace and Erica

☐ just Erica   ☐ neither Grace nor Erica

> What a hoot.

ii) Explain your answer.

....

....

....

....

....

....

When combined with water, lithium hypochlorite (LiClO) reacts to form hypochlorous acid (HOCl), which can remove colour from objects. One other product is also formed.

b) Use the diagram above to suggest why the other product **can't** be an element.

....

....

....

....

c) Suggest the formula for potassium hypochlorite: ....

Ceramics, Polymers and Composites

1. Complete this paragraph using words from the word bank below.

mixed	carbon	natural	nitrogen	bonded	compound	thousands
random	glued	pretty	man-made	tens	mixture	repeating

A polymer is a .... made up of very long molecules.

Polymers are made by joining .... of smaller molecules together

in a .... pattern. Starch is an example of a ....

polymer. It contains lots of little molecules called sugars, which are chemically

.... together in a chain. Plants make starch to store energy. Most

polymers, including starch, contain the element ....

2. Draw lines to match each material to its type and description.

CONCRETE	ceramic	A plastic that is soft and flexible.
NYLON	polymer	A mixture of sand and gravel embedded in cement.
PORCELAIN	composite	A brittle material that is an insulator of heat.

3. Carrier bags are often made from polythene, which is a polymer.

a) Is polythene a man-made polymer or a natural polymer?

☐ man-made   ☐ natural

b) Give two properties of polythene that make it suitable for making carrier bags.

1. ....

2. ....

c) Why wouldn't it be a good idea to make a carrier bag out of a ceramic material?

....

....

....

Topic 8 — Compounds

Ceramics, Polymers and Composites

4. Greenhouses are used to keep plants warm and protected. They have transparent walls, which let sunlight in. Jodie wants to build a greenhouse in her garden. She can make the greenhouse using either glass or thin, clear sheets of PVC.

SCIENCE
IN ACTION

a) What sort of compound is...

   i) glass? ....

   ii) PVC? ....

b) Use the information in the table and your own knowledge to explain the advantages and disadvantages of using each material to build the greenhouse.
Which one do you think Jodie should choose?

Material	Cost	Appearance
Glass	medium	does not change
PVC	low	turns cloudy over time

....

....

....

....

....

....

....

....

c) i) Fibreglass is made from glass fibres embedded in plastic.

     What sort of material is fibreglass? ....

  ii) Why might fibreglass be a better material for the greenhouse than glass or PVC?

....

....

....

How did you do?

That's another topic done and dusted. Hopefully now you're cool as a cucumber when it comes to:

☐ Knowing what molecules and compounds are.

☐ Identifying substances from particle diagrams.

☐ Working out the names of compounds.

☐ Using chemical formulae.

☐ Identifying substances from reactions.

☐ Describing properties of ceramics, polymers and composites.

Topic 9 — Types of Reaction

I hope your reaction to this page isn't one of complete despair — here's some more reactions to learn...

Learning Objectives

1. Understand that mass is always conserved in a reaction.
2. Know what happens in a combustion reaction.
3. Know what happens in a thermal decomposition reaction.
4. Be able to represent reactions using formulae and balance equations.

$4Fe + 3O_2 \rightarrow 2Fe_2O_3$

Before you Start

1. **Are these sentences true or false? Tick the correct box.**

		True	False
a)	New substances are formed in physical changes.	☐	☐
b)	Only metals can be oxidised in oxidation reactions.	☐	☐
c)	Metal oxides are bases that can neutralise acids.	☐	☐
d)	Neutralisation is a type of displacement reaction.	☐	☐
e)	In a displacement reaction, a less reactive metal will displace a more reactive metal.	☐	☐

2. **Circle any of the diagrams that show a compound.**

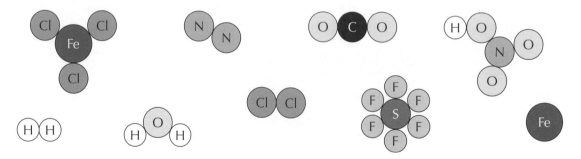

3. **Are these reactions an oxidation (O) or displacement (D)? Write an O or D next to each reaction.**

   a) hydrochloric acid + copper oxide → copper chloride + water   ....

   b) ethane + oxygen → carbon dioxide + water   ....

   c) sulfur + oxygen → sulfur dioxide   ....

   d) chlorine + sodium bromide → sodium chloride + bromine   ....

Chemical Reactions

1. Complete this paragraph using the following words.

| after | before | conserved | products | reactants | rearranged |

In a chemical reaction, the atoms and molecules are .... to form

new substances. Chemical reactions can be shown using word and symbol equations.

The .... are the substances that you start with, shown ....

the arrow in an equation. The .... are the substances that you end up with,

shown .... the arrow in an equation. The total mass is ....

— it does not change.

2. Diagrams can be used to show what happens in a reaction.

a) This diagram shows the neutralisation of magnesium oxide by hydrochloric acid.

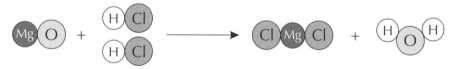

   i) What is the word equation for this reaction?

   ....

   ii) Explain why there are two molecules of hydrochloric acid as reactants.

   ....

   ....

b) The symbol equation for the displacement reaction between magnesium and copper sulfate
   is $Mg + CuSO_4 \rightarrow MgSO_4 + Cu$. Use this to complete the diagram for this reaction.

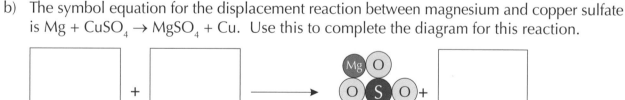

c) Write out a balanced symbol equation for the reaction below.

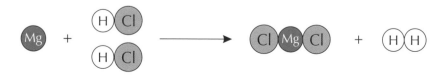

   ....

Topic 9 — Types of Reaction

Chemical Reactions

3. Charlie is observing mass during different reactions.

a) She adds 5 g of zinc powder to 50 g of hydrochloric acid in a beaker. A reaction occurs and the total mass of the beaker changes.

acid
zinc
reaction
55.00 g
54.85 g

   i) Write down the word equation for this reaction between a metal and an acid.

   ....

   ii) Why did the mass of the beaker change?

   ....

   ....

b) Charlie adds 5 g of zinc hydroxide powder to 25 g of hydrochloric acid in a different beaker. A reaction occurs but the total mass of the beaker stays the same.

   i) Zinc hydroxide is an alkali.
   What type of reaction is this? ....

   ii) Name the two products of this reaction.

   1. ....

   2. ....

   iii) Explain why the total mass of the beaker did not change in this reaction.

   ....

   ....

c) Charlie puts 10 g of gallium metal into a third beaker. Gallium melts at around 30 °C.

   i) What effect would the gallium melting have on the total mass of the beaker?

   ....

   ii) Charlie carries out an oxidation of the gallium. After the reaction, the mass in the beaker is 13.44 g. What mass of oxygen reacted in this reaction?

   MATHS SKILLS

   ....

   iii) Finish balancing the symbol equation for this reaction.

   $$4Ga \quad + \quad .... \ O_2 \quad \longrightarrow \quad .... \ Ga_2O_3$$

Combustion and Thermal Decomposition

1. Combustion is a type of oxidation reaction.
Circle the correct words in this paragraph about combustion.

Combustion reactions require a fuel, heat and **oxygen / carbon**. Fuels store

energy in a(n) **chemical / electrical** store. When fuels are burned, they transfer

this energy to the thermal energy stores of the surroundings. Hydrocarbons are

a type of fuel that contain **hydrogen / water** and carbon. When hydrocarbons

burn, the combustion reaction produces water and **hydrogen / carbon dioxide**.

2. Toby heats some magnesium carbonate in an open test tube. A reaction occurs.

PRACTICAL

a) The word equation for this reaction is:
magnesium carbonate → magnesium oxide + carbon dioxide

   i) What type of reaction is this?

   ....

   ii) Explain how you can tell.

   ....

   ....

b) Toby says, "This must be a physical change, because there is only one reactant."
Explain why Toby is wrong.

   ....

   ....

c) Suggest a way that Toby could confirm that a gas is given off during the reaction.

   ....

   ....

d) Toby carries out the same steps with some other substances.
All the reactions give out carbon dioxide. Predict the other product of each reaction.

   i) calcium carbonate ....

   ii) copper carbonate ....

   iii) lead carbonate ....

Topic 9 — Types of Reaction

Combustion and Thermal Decomposition

3. Methane is a hydrocarbon that is used as fuel in gas stoves.
Propane is another hydrocarbon that is used as a fuel.

SCIENCE IN ACTION

a) Write down the word equation for the combustion of methane.

....

b) If a combustion reaction isn't well-ventilated, other substances can be produced.
Here is the word equation for the combustion of propane in a poorly-ventilated room.

propane + oxygen $\longrightarrow$ carbon monoxide + carbon + water

Balance the symbol equation for this reaction. Not every substance needs a number.

.... C_3H_8 + ... O_2 $\longrightarrow$ .... CO + $4C$ + ... H_2O

The table below shows some possible products of combustion and their properties.

Substance	Property
carbon (C)	given off as soot
carbon monoxide (CO)	toxic gas
carbon dioxide (CO_2)	greenhouse gas
sulfur dioxide (SO_2)	dissolves in water to form an acid

c) Fuels containing sulfur compounds can cause acid rain. Why do you think this is?

....

....

d) Hydrogen can also be used as a fuel. Water is the only product
when hydrogen combusts. Why do you think burning hydrogen
might be better for the environment than burning propane?

....

....

....

How did you do?

This book won't thermally decompose but it could combust... Don't get any ideas, though —
you need to take a minute and make sure that you:

☐ Understand that mass is always
conserved in a reaction.

☐ Know what happens in a thermal
decomposition reaction.

☐ Know what happens in a
combustion reaction.

☐ Are able to represent reactions using
formulae and balance equations.

Topic 9 — Types of Reaction

☹ ☐　　😐 ☐　　😉 ☐

Topic 10 — Chemical Energy

Might be worth grabbing a biscuit for some energy to tackle the next topic...

Learning Objectives

1. Know the difference between an exothermic and an endothermic reaction.
2. Understand that bonds are broken and new bonds formed during a chemical reaction.
3. Know that bond breaking requires energy and that bond formation releases energy.
4. Be able to interpret energy level diagrams for different reactions.
5. Know that a catalyst can speed up a reaction without being used up.

Before you Start

1. **As ice melts to water, the water molecules gain energy.**

   a) For each change of state below, where does the energy come from?

   i) An ice cube melts to water at room temperature. ....

   ii) An ice cube melts over a flame and then boils. ....

   b) Why does one ice cube end up boiling, but the other one doesn't?

   ....

   ....

2. **True or False:**

	True	False
a) Combustion reactions always involve hydrogen.	☐	☐
b) The amount of mass does not change in a chemical reaction.	☐	☐
c) In thermal decomposition, a single reactant is broken down.	☐	☐
d) Fuel stores energy in a kinetic energy store.	☐	☐

3. **Balance these symbol equations.**

   a) .... Al + ... S → Al_2S_3

   b) .... Na + $2H_2O$ → .... NaOH + H_2

   c) C_3H_8 + ... O_2 → .... CO_2 + ... H_2O

58

Exothermic and Endothermic Reactions

1. In a chemical reaction, energy is transferred to or from the surroundings. Circle the correct words in this paragraph about different reactions.

An exothermic reaction is one where energy is **transferred to / taken in from** the surroundings. The temperature of the surroundings **increases / decreases** because the energy of the surroundings has **decreased / increased**. An endothermic reaction is one where energy is **transferred to / taken in from** the surroundings. The temperature of the surroundings **increases / decreases**.

2. Different types of reaction transfer different amounts of energy.

a) A combustion reaction is an example of an exothermic reaction. Explain why.

....

....

b) A thermal decomposition reaction is usually endothermic. Why do you think this is?

....

....

3. Some disposable hand warmers use the oxidation of iron to give out heat. When the hand warmer is removed from its plastic packet, it gets warm.

SCIENCE IN ACTION

a) Is the oxidation of iron an exothermic or endothermic reaction? Explain your answer.

....

....

b) Why doesn't the hand warmer warm up until it's taken out of the packet?

....

....

c) Balance the symbol equation for this reaction.

.... Fe + ... $O_2 \longrightarrow$ .... Fe_2O_3

Exothermic and Endothermic Reactions

4. Jaden is investigating how different salts dissolve in water. He dissolves 10 g of each salt in 50 ml of water.

a) He measures the temperature of the water before and after the salt has dissolved. His results are shown in the table below.

Salt	Initial Water Temperature (°C)	Final Water Temperature (°C)	Exothermic or Endothermic?
ammonium nitrate	25.3	14.2	
calcium chloride	24.8	49.9	
sodium chloride	25.1	22.9	

i) What is the temperature change of the water with calcium chloride?

....°C

ii) Complete the fourth column of the table to say whether each process is exothermic or endothermic.

b) Instant cold packs are often used as first aid for sports injuries. A cold pack is made up of two parts — one part contains salt crystals, and the other contains water. When the bag is squeezed for use, the water can mix with the salt. These packs cannot be reused.

i) Which salt from Jaden's experiment is best suited for use in a cold pack?

....

ii) What do you think would happen if Jaden dissolved 20 g of this salt instead, in the same volume of water?

....

....

iii) Which of the salts from Jaden's experiment would be best for making a heat pack?

....

c) Some heat packs contain a solution of sodium acetate. The solution releases heat when it crystallises. Crystallisation is the opposite process to dissolving. The crystals can be redissolved by boiling the pack in water.

Suggest why these heat packs are preferred over ones that work by mixing a salt and water?

....

....

Energy Levels and Bond Energies

1. Circle the correct words in this paragraph about chemical bonds.

A chemical bond is the force that holds atoms together in **molecules / love**. Energy is **made / transferred** when bonds are broken or formed. In a chemical reaction, bonds in the **reactants / products** are broken, which uses heat energy. New chemical bonds are formed in the **reactants / products**, releasing heat energy. Whether a reaction is exothermic or endothermic depends on the overall energy difference between bond breaking and forming.

2. An energy level diagram shows the change in energy between the reactants and the products during a reaction. Energy level diagrams for three neutralisation reactions are shown below. They all use the same scale and can be compared to each other.

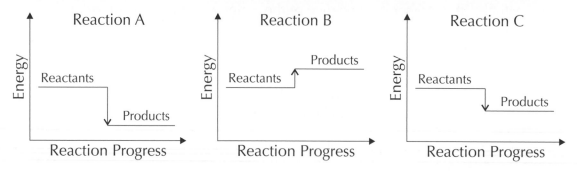

Kelly carries out the three reactions in three separate beakers. She measures the temperature change of the solution as each reaction takes place.

a) She says that the reaction with the greatest increase in temperature must be reaction B. Explain why she is incorrect.   **PRACTICAL**

....

....

b) She then says that neutralisation reaction A releases more energy than reaction C. Explain why she is correct.

....

....

c) Complete the table using the reactions shown in the energy level diagrams above.

Beaker	Temperature Change	Exothermic or Endothermic?	Reaction A, B or C?
1	–4.4 °C		
2	+5.6 °C		
3	+7.1 °C		

Energy Levels and Bond Energies

3. Different reactions have different changes in energy.

a) Match each of the energy changes from the box to one of the energy level diagrams.
The energy level diagrams all use the same scale.

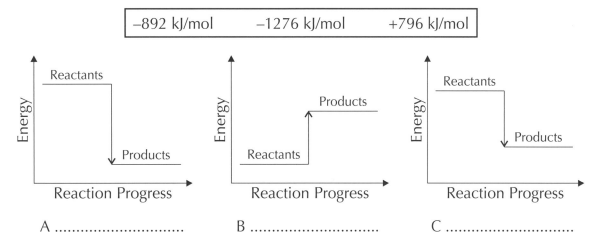

| −892 kJ/mol | −1276 kJ/mol | +796 kJ/mol |

A ....   B ....   C ....

b) Give the letters of any of the energy level diagrams that could show the
change in energy in a combustion reaction. Explain your answer.

....

....

4. Plants are able to make their own food by converting
carbon dioxide and water into sugar and oxygen.

a) Balance the symbol equation for this reaction.

.... CO_2 + ... H_2O $\longrightarrow$ $C_6H_{12}O_6$ + ... O_2

The amount of energy required to break bonds in this reaction is 15 204 kJ/mol.
The amount of energy released on bond forming is 12 520 kJ/mol.

b) Calculate the overall energy change for this reaction.

..........................kJ/mol

c) Is this reaction exothermic or endothermic?

....

d) This reaction can only take place when it is light.
Using your answer to part c), why do you think this is?

....

....

Topic 10 — Chemical Energy

Energy Levels and Bond Energies

5. Amelia is using data for energy changes to predict reactions.

a) Hydrogen can react with halogens to form hydrogen halides, such as hydrogen chloride. The energy change for each of the first four halogen reactions is shown in the table.

Halogen	Reaction	Energy Change
Fluorine	$H_2 + F_2 \rightarrow 2HF$	−543 kJ/mol
Chlorine	$H_2 + Cl_2 \rightarrow 2HCl$	−185 kJ/mol
Bromine	$H_2 + Br_2 \rightarrow 2HBr$	−103 kJ/mol
Iodine	$H_2 + I_2 \rightarrow 2HI$	−11 kJ/mol

i) Which of these four halogen reactions is the most exothermic? ....

ii) Which of these four halogen reactions will release the least energy? ....

b) The reverse of this reaction is decomposition.
A hydrogen halide breaks down to form hydrogen and the halogen.

If a reaction gives out energy, its reverse reaction will take in the same amount of energy.

i) Amelia says that the decomposition reaction will be endothermic. Explain why she is correct.

....

....

....

ii) Of these four hydrogen halides, hydrogen iodide will decompose most easily. Explain why.

....

....

....

c) Amelia compares her information with that for the reaction of hydrogen and oxygen.

i) The energy required to break the reactant bonds ($2H_2 + O_2$) is 1370 kJ/mol and the energy released on formation of the product bonds ($2H_2O$) is 1856 kJ/mol. Calculate the energy difference for this reaction.

MATHS SKILLS

....

ii) Which is more exothermic, the formation of water or the formation of hydrogen fluoride? Explain why.

....

....

Catalysts

1. True or False:

True False

a) A catalyst speeds up a reaction. ☐ ☐

b) The mass of the catalyst decreases during the reaction. ☐ ☐

c) All reactions can be catalysed by the same catalyst. ☐ ☐

d) Catalysts only work for endothermic reactions. ☐ ☐

2. A power plant releases carbon dioxide into the atmosphere, which is a pollutant. A new catalyst is available that catalyses a reaction that turns the carbon dioxide to methanol, which can be used as fuel. The new catalyst needs a lot of new equipment to be installed.

a) Give one benefit for the factory if it decides to use the new catalyst.

....

b) Give one disadvantage for the factory if it decides to use the new catalyst.

....

3. Car exhaust systems contain a device called a catalytic converter.
This reduces the amount of harmful substances released by the exhaust.

SCIENCE IN ACTION

a) Balance the symbol equation for this reaction that takes place in a catalytic converter.

.... CO + ... $NO \longrightarrow$ .... N_2 + ... CO_2

b) Platinum is often used as a catalyst in catalytic converters, but it is very expensive. Henry and Linda are talking about catalytic converters.

> Henry: The platinum in a catalytic converter will need replacing often because it will get used up.

> Linda: You don't have to use platinum in a catalytic converter — any metal would work as a catalyst and would make it cheaper.

What do you think about what Henry and Linda have said?

....

....

....

Catalysts

4. Harvey is investigating the effect of different catalysts on the decomposition of hydrogen peroxide.

a) Hydrogen peroxide decomposes to form water and oxygen.
   Balance the symbol equation for this reaction.

   .... H_2O_2 $\longrightarrow$ .... H_2O + ... O_2

b) Harvey carries out the experiment in four measuring cylinders. Each cylinder contains 50 cm³ of hydrogen peroxide solution and a few drops of washing-up liquid. He uses equal quantities of powdered forms of the catalysts. The oxygen produced forms a foam with the washing-up liquid.

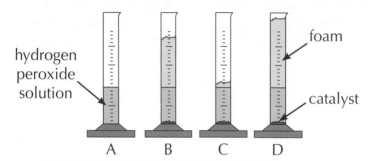

Cylinder	Catalyst
A	no catalyst
B	manganese oxide
C	iron oxide
D	lead oxide

   i) Why hasn't Harvey added a catalyst to cylinder A?

   ....

   ii) Compare how effective each catalyst is at increasing the rate of decomposition.

   ....

   ....

c) The energy required to break the reactant bonds in this reaction is 2148 kJ/mol and the energy released on formation of the product bonds in this reaction is 2354 kJ/mol. Use this information to work out whether the foam will be warm or cold.

   ....

   ....

   ....

Topic 11 — Climate

Life is pretty dependent on Earth's atmosphere and climate, but humans are causing both to change...

Learning Objectives

1. Know the composition of Earth's atmosphere.
2. Know how carbon is recycled in the environment through natural processes and human activities.
3. Understand how greenhouse gases affect global temperatures.
4. Understand how human activity is linked to climate change.

This one has a great atmosphere.

Before you Start

1. **Tick the box that correctly completes the sentence below.**

   The Earth's temperature is...

   ☐ ...decreasing.   ☐ ...increasing.   ☐ ...staying the same.

2. **Listed below are some sources used to generate electricity. Circle all the fossil fuels.**

   Coal   Waves   Crude oil

   Biomass   Sun   Wind   Natural gas

3. **How are fossil fuels formed? Tick the correct box.**

   ☐ Machines are used to heat and compress dead plants and animal waste.

   ☐ Dead organisms are buried in the Earth and decay over millions of years.

   ☐ Rocks are melted at high temperatures to make them liquid.

4. **Fossil fuels contain hydrocarbons. Complete the word equation below for the combustion of hydrocarbons.**

   hydrocarbon + oxygen ⟶ .... + water

5. **Do you think the statements below are true or false? Tick the correct boxes.**

		True	False
a)	Climate and weather are the same thing.	☐	☐
b)	The climate of an area is its average temperature.	☐	☐
c)	The climate of an area includes wind, rain and temperature.	☐	☐
d)	The climate of an area includes the times when the sun rises.	☐	☐
e)	The climate of an area can change over time.	☐	☐

Earth's Atmosphere

1. Answer the questions below about the Earth's atmosphere.

   a) Which of the following sentences is the correct definition of the Earth's atmosphere?
   Tick the correct box.

   ☐ All the oxygen and carbon dioxide that is in the air.

   ☐ All the layers of gases that surround the Earth.

   ☐ The outer layer of the Earth, between the surface and the mantle.

   ☐ The gases that are within 1 km of the surface of the Earth.

   b) The pie chart below shows what the Earth's atmosphere is made from.
   Fill in the labels using the words in the box below.

   | carbon dioxide   nitrogen   oxygen |

   <1% other gases,
   including:

   21% ....

   ....

   78% ....

2. Planet Ulvertron has a different atmosphere to Earth. The gases present in Ulvertron's atmosphere are shown in the table on the right.

   a) Work out the percentage of Ulvertron's atmosphere that is oxygen.

Gas	Percentage of atmosphere
Carbon dioxide	79.32
Nitrogen	5.31
Argon	11.42
Oxygen	
Carbon monoxide	1.69
Other gases	2.17

   ....%

   b) Suggest why the atmosphere on Ulvertron would make it difficult for humans to survive there.

   ....

   ....

Carbon Cycle

1. The diagram below shows part of the carbon cycle.

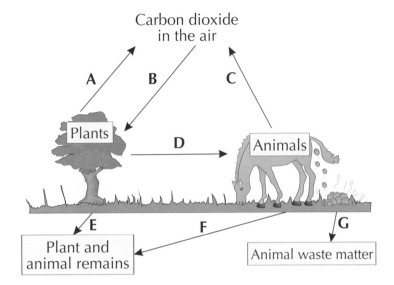

Carbon dioxide in the air

A   B   C

Plants

D

Animals

E   F   G

Plant and animal remains

Animal waste matter

a) Photosynthesis and respiration are two processes that are important in the carbon cycle. Photosynthesis is the process in which plants make their own food using carbon dioxide and water. Respiration is a process carried out by all living organisms in which energy is transferred from glucose and carbon dioxide is released as a by-product.

Which letter (or letters) on the diagram, A-G, do you think represent:

i) Photosynthesis? ....   ii) Respiration? ....

b) Animal waste matter is broken down and used as food by decomposers, such as dung beetles and bacteria. Some of the carbon from the waste they feed on gets returned to the atmosphere.

i) How do you think this happens?

....

ii) Suggest why not all of the carbon in the decomposers' food is returned to the atmosphere.

....

....

c) If plant and animal remains aren't decomposed they can remain in the Earth for many years. Eventually, human activities can cause the carbon they contain to be released back into the atmosphere. Explain how.

....

....

Carbon Cycle

2. Human activities can affect the carbon cycle. Some of this is because carbon sinks, such as forests, are being lost.

a) i) What is a carbon sink?

....

ii) Give two examples of carbon sinks, other than areas of vegetation such as forests.

1. .... 2. ....

b) In some areas, large areas of forest have been cut down to build cities. Suggest how this change in land use has affected the carbon dioxide concentration in the atmosphere.

....

....

....

c) Biofuels can be made from plants, which can then be used to fuel vehicles through combustion. Biofuels are considered carbon neutral, meaning that they neither increase or decrease the overall carbon dioxide concentration in the atmosphere. Suggest how this is achieved.

SCIENCE IN ACTION

....

....

3. As the carbon dioxide concentration of the atmosphere increases, the carbon dioxide concentration of the oceans increases. Scientists think this is making the oceans more acidic.

a) How does carbon dioxide enter the oceans from the atmosphere?

....

b) Suggest how human activities are affecting the amount of carbon dioxide in the oceans.

....

c) Blowing through a straw into a liquid increases the carbon dioxide concentration of the liquid. Suggest how a student could use a straw, a pH meter and a beaker of sea water to model the effect on acidity of increasing the carbon dioxide concentration of sea water.

....

....

....

Climate Change

1. There is growing concern about the effects that climate change might have on our planet.

    a) Circle the correct words to complete the sentence below.

        Scientists have evidence to suggest that **climate change** / **global warming** brought about by **natural** / **human** activity is causing **climate change** / **global warming**.

    b) Suggest two examples of climate change that scientists might be worried about.

        1. ....   2. ....

2. Answer the questions below about the greenhouse effect and global warming.

    a) What is meant by the term 'global warming'?

        ....

    b) Name one greenhouse gas that contributes to global warming. ....

    c) Which of the diagrams below illustrates the greenhouse effect? Tick the correct box.

Sun A ☐	Sun B ☐

◠	Atmosphere
▬	Earth
⇨	Energy from Sun
→	Heat radiation

    d) Explain the link between the greenhouse effect and global warming.

        ....

        ....

        ....

        ....

        ....

3. In an attempt to reduce carbon dioxide (CO_2) emissions, some governments are planning on making electric cars the only option for people buying a new car.

When an electric car is charged, electricity is used to transfer energy to the battery. For every kWh of energy transferred, 350 g of CO_2 was produced when the electricity was generated.

    a) Ruby's electric car uses 18.5 kWh of energy every 100 km she drives. How much CO_2 is created for each kilometre driven? Give your answer in grams.

.... g

Topic 11 — Climate

Climate Change

b) A petrol car produces 105 g of CO_2 per km. Ruby says, 'If everyone drove electric cars, global warming wouldn't be an issue.' Discuss whether you agree or disagree with Ruby.

....

....

....

4. Henri knows that increases carbon dioxide (CO_2) in the atmosphere leads to global warming due to the greenhouse effect. He's researching how human activities are linked to CO_2 in the atmosphere. Three pieces of evidence he's been looking at are shown below.

Graph A

World population
1000-2000

World population
(billion people)

Year

Graph B

Atmospheric carbon dioxide
concentration 1958-2018

Carbon dioxide
concentration (ppm)

Year

Textbook extract: "There's evidence to suggest that for hundreds of thousands of years before about 1900, carbon dioxide concentration regularly fluctuated between about 180 and 300 ppm. Since the early 1900s it's been above 300 ppm consistently."

Do you think the evidence Henri has collected suggests that humans are causing an increase in CO_2 in the atmosphere? Explain your answer.

....

....

....

....

....

....

How did you do?

The changing climate affects all life on earth, so I'd say it's pretty darn important. Make sure you:

☐ Know the composition of the atmosphere.

☐ Understand the effect of greenhouse gases.

☐ Know what happens in the carbon cycle and understand how humans affect it.

☐ Understand the link between human activity, global warming and climate change.

Topic 12 — Earth Resources

Many of the important materials we need are in limited supply, so we've got to be careful not to run out.

Learning Objectives

1. Know that metals are usually found as compounds in ores.

2. Understand that different methods can be used to extract metals from ores, depending on the reactivity of the metal.

3. Know that the Earth has limited natural resources.

4. Understand how recycling helps to conserve the Earth's natural resources.

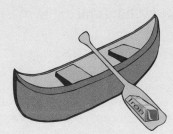

Before you Start

1. **Which of the sentences below is the correct definition of a metal compound? Tick the correct box.**

   ☐ A mixture of a metal and another element.

   ☐ A solid metal.

   ☐ A metal joined with another element by a chemical bond.

   ☐ A metal that has been squashed into a thin sheet.

2. **What is shown by a reactivity series? Tick the correct box.**

   ☐ All the metals that need extracting from ores.

   ☐ Elements in order of their reactivity towards other elements.

   ☐ All the elements that react with carbon.

3. **The word equation for a displacement reaction is shown below.**

   copper sulfate + zinc ⟶ copper + zinc sulfate

   Circle the correct words in the following sentences.

   A **more / less** reactive metal will displace a **more / less** reactive metal from a compound.

   In the reaction shown above, **copper / zinc** has displaced **copper / zinc**.

4. **A current is put in a solution that contains molecules with charges (ions). Complete the diagram to show where the different molecules (ions) will move to.**

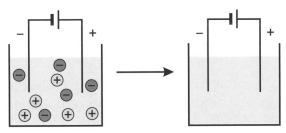

Extraction Methods

1. Ores provide us with minerals, which can be used to make lots of different things.

   a) What is meant by the following words:

      i) Mineral? ....

      ii) Ore? ....

   b) Why do metals usually have to be extracted from ores before they can be used?

      ....

      ....

   c) Using the reactivity series on the right, explain why iron can be extracted from its ore using carbon, but aluminium can't.

      Magnesium ↑
      Aluminium
      Carbon   Increasing
      Iron   reactivity
      Copper

      ....

      ....

      ....

   d) Aluminium can be extracted by passing an electric current through liquid aluminium oxide (an ore of aluminium). Liquid aluminium oxide contains positively charged aluminium atoms and negatively charged oxygen atoms.

      SCIENCE IN ACTION

      i) Circle the correct words in the passage below.

         To extract aluminium, **displacement** / **electrolysis** is used. This process separates

         some **elements** / **compounds** into **elements** / **compounds** . This process uses **more**

         / **less** energy and is **more** / **less** expensive than extracting metals using carbon.

      ii) Suggest how aluminium is extracted from aluminium oxide by the method described.

         ....

         ....

         ....

      iii) Suggest one thing that the extracted aluminium could be used for.

         ....

   e) Other than the type of extraction method they'd use, suggest one factor that a mining company may consider when deciding whether or not to mine a new ore they find.

      ....

Recycling Resources

1. Iona has recycling bins for several types of household waste, including glass, plastic and paper. Recycling reduces the impact that humans have on Earth's natural resources.

a) What is recycling?

....

b) i) Iona uses some of her old drinks cans as plant pots. She says this is recycling. Do you agree or disagree with Iona? Explain your answer.

....

....

ii) Suggest two other ways that Iona could reduce her use of natural resources.

1. ....

2. ....

c) Explain why recycling is important for protecting Earth's natural resources.

....

....

....

2. Mobile phones contain small amounts of several rare metals, such as gold, silver and palladium. Many smartphones are used for a few years before being replaced.

a) Micah is considering starting a business to recycle the metal contained inside mobile phones. Micah estimates that the average mobile phone contains 0.016 g of palladium, 0.3 g of silver and 0.035 g of gold.

i) Micah can sell palladium for £37.50 per g, silver for 38p per g and gold for £31.00 per g. How much money could he make from recycling these metals from one mobile phone?

£................................

ii) Micah will need to spend £1 million on machinery to be able to recycle mobile phones. How many phones will he need to recycle to make this money back?

You'll need to use your answer to part i) here.

.... phones

Topic 12 — Earth Resources

Recycling Resources

b) Suggest why recycling metals from mobile phones may be particularly important.

....

....

....

c) Suggest one other way that waste from the mobile phone industry could be reduced.

....

....

3. Sasha compares the energy that can be saved from recycling different metals instead of extracting them from their ores.

SCIENCE IN ACTION

a) Why do you think recycling metals instead of extracting them from ores saves energy?

....

....

....

....

Material	Energy saved (%)
Aluminium	95
Steel	60

b) Steel is made from iron and carbon. Using what you know about the reactivity of iron and aluminium, suggest why more energy is saved by recycling aluminium than by recycling steel.

Take a look back at the reactivity series on p.72 if you need to.

....

....

....

....

How did you do?

That's it — you've extracted all you can from these pages. Now it's time to see if you've been able to recycle everything you know by ticking off this checklist. By now, you should:

☐ Know that metals are found in ores.

☐ Understand why different methods may be used to extract metals from ores.

☐ Know that the Earth has limited resources.

☐ Understand why recycling is important.

Topic 13 — Breathing

Take a deep breath in — and breathe out. It's time to learn about breathing...

Learning Objectives

1. Know the structure and function of the gas exchange system.
2. Understand how the structures of the gas exchange system are adapted to their functions.
3. Understand the mechanism of breathing, and the volume and pressure changes involved.
4. Understand how a model can show the mechanism of breathing.
5. Be able to explain how exercise, asthma and smoking affect the gas exchange system.

Before you Start

1. **Which of these sentences is true and which is false?
   Tick the correct box.**

		true	false
a)	The blood transports oxygen to the cells.	☐	☐
b)	Ribs are bones.	☐	☐
c)	We breathe out a smaller amount of air than we breathe in.	☐	☐
d)	We only breathe in oxygen.	☐	☐
e)	The diaphragm is a muscle.	☐	☐

2. **Which organ is important for breathing? Circle the correct answer.**

   kidney   lungs   stomach   small intestine   liver

3. **In which of these situations would your breathing rate be the highest?
   Circle the correct answer.**

   A   B   C   D

4. **Sarah has an asthma attack. What effect do you think that this has on her breathing?
   Tick the correct box.**

   ☐ Her breathing is normal.   ☐ Breathing is more difficult for her.

   ☐ Breathing is easier for her
      when she is doing exercise.

Gas Exchange

1. Complete the table below. Write the name of the structure found in the gas exchange system that matches the description provided, or write a description for the structure provided.

Structure	Description
a)	a tube that carries air from the mouth and nose to the lungs
bronchi	b) ....
c)	small tubes in the lungs
d)	a sheet of muscle found underneath the lungs
alveoli	e) ....
ribcage	f) ....

2. Circle the correct words in this paragraph about gas exchange.

Air is drawn into the **lungs / heart** where gas exchange takes place. In gas exchange, oxygen and carbon dioxide move between the **alveoli / trachea** and the blood.

Oxygen / carbon dioxide passes into the bloodstream and is transported to cells.

Oxygen / carbon dioxide passes out of the bloodstream to be breathed out.

Gases pass into or out of the bloodstream by **diffusion / conduction**.

3. The lungs are well-adapted for gas exchange. Explain how the following adaptations help the lungs carry out gas exchange efficiently.

a) The lungs have many alveoli.

....

....

b) The lungs have a good blood supply.

....

....

Gas Exchange

4. The diagram below shows one alveolus in the lung.

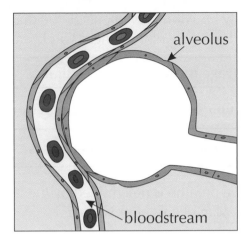

a) Add two labelled arrows to the diagram above to show the movement of oxygen and carbon dioxide between the alveolus and the bloodstream.

b) A person has just breathed in. Complete the two tables below to show the concentrations of gases in their bloodstream compared to the concentrations in their alveolus. Use the words '**HIGH**' or '**LOW**'.

BLOODSTREAM	
Gas	**Concentration**
Oxygen	
Carbon dioxide	

ALVEOLUS	
Gas	**Concentration**
Oxygen	
Carbon dioxide	

c) Carbon dioxide is present in body cells. Why is this? Tick the correct box.

☐ Carbon dioxide is a reactant of respiration in body cells.

☐ Carbon dioxide is a waste product of digestion in body cells.

☐ Carbon dioxide is a waste product of respiration in body cells.

5. Emphysema is a disease that causes the walls of the alveoli to break down. What effect do you think this has on the efficiency of gas exchange? Explain why.

....

....

....

The Mechanism of Breathing

1. The movements of the diaphragm and the ribcage are important in breathing.

a) Complete this table to show how the movements of the diaphragm and the ribcage cause changes in the volume and pressure of the lungs. Circle each correct answer.

Diaphragm moves...	Ribcage moves...	Volume...	Pressure...
down	**up / down**	increases	**increases / decreases**
up / down	down	decreases	**increases / decreases**

b) Marcella says, 'How fast we breathe is determined by the amount of oxygen required by body cells.' Is Marcella right or wrong?

....

2. The bell jar model below can be used to demonstrate the process of breathing.

a) Which part of the respiratory system do the following parts of the bell jar represent:

   i) the tube? ....

   ii) the bell jar? ....

   iii) the rubber sheet? ....

tube

bell jar

balloon

rubber sheet

b) Suggest one difference between the balloons and the lungs.

....

....

c) When the rubber sheet is pushed up into the bell jar, the balloons deflate. Explain why this happens.

....

....

....

d) Donna says that, "to inflate the balloons, you have to blow into the tube." Why is she wrong? Explain how to inflate the balloons without blowing into the tube.

....

....

....

The Mechanism of Breathing

3. Carlos and Jane are investigating whether their lung volume is linked to their height. Carlos is 150 cm tall and Jane is 126 cm.

PRACTICAL

a) What is lung volume?

....

....

b) Carlos and Jane are making predictions for their experiment.

Carlos: I'm taller than you, so I'll have a bigger lung volume than you.

Jane: Height can't be linked to lung volume. Our lung volume will be the same.

Whose prediction would you expect to be right? Explain your answer.

....

....

Carlos and Jane each measure their lung volume three times. Here are their results:

Breath	Carlos' Lung Volume (mL)	Jane's Lung Volume (mL)
1	4600	4580
2	4695	4600
3	4550	4650

c) i) Calculate the mean lung volume for both Carlos and Jane.

MATHS SKILLS

Carlos: .... mL   Jane: .... mL

ii) What do these results show? Who made the correct prediction?

....

....

d) Lisa is trying to predict her lung volume based on her height. She is 136 cm tall. She thinks her lung volume will be smaller than Jane's. Why is she likely to be wrong?

....

....

Exercise, Asthma and Smoking

1. Elliot visits a petting zoo. During his visit he has an asthma attack.

a) Why do you think Elliot has had an asthma attack?

....

b) What has happened to parts of his breathing system during the asthma attack?

....

....

2. The graph below shows the breathing rate for two runners before, during and after a run.

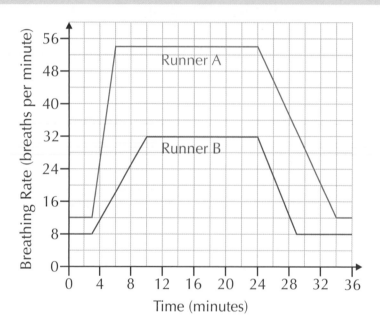

a) At what time did the runners start their run? How can you tell?

.... minutes

....

b) The runners ran at the same speed and then stopped immediately.
How long do you think the run lasted for?

.... minutes

c) i) How long did it take for each runner's breathing rate
to return to normal after they stopped running?

Runner A: .... minutes   Runner B: .... minutes

Exercise, Asthma and Smoking

ii) Complete the table below, using information from the graph.

	Starting Breathing Rate (breaths per minute)	Peak Breathing Rate (breaths per minute)	Percentage Increase (%)
Runner A			
Runner B			

d) i) Which of the following do you think will result from regular exercise? Tick the correct box.

☐ bigger feet   ☐ stronger diaphragm   ☐ fewer alveoli

ii) Based on peak breathing rate, which runner do you think exercises more regularly?

....

....

....

....

3. Smoking decreases the efficiency of gas exchange, which affects the body.

a) Why do you think some smokers become out of breath when going for a short walk?

....

....

....

b) Do you think smoking will increase or decrease the rate of respiration? Explain why.

....

....

How did you do?

Breathing is an automatic process, but understanding the breathing process isn't. By now you should:

☐ Know the structure and function of the gas exchange system.

☐ Understand the mechanism of breathing.

☐ Understand a model of breathing.

☐ Be able to explain how exercise, asthma and smoking affect the gas exchange system.

Topic 14 — Respiration

Breathe in and out, and then remember this — respiration is NOT breathing. It's actually all about energy...

Learning Objectives

1. Know that respiration involves breaking down glucose to provide energy for life.
2. Know the word equations for aerobic and anaerobic respiration.
3. Understand the differences between aerobic and anaerobic respiration.
4. Understand the process of fermentation and its uses.

Before you Start

1. **Circle the organisms below which need energy to function.**

2. **Tick any true sentences below about energy in the body.**

☐ Fats are the only source of energy for the body.
☐ The body uses energy to move around.

☐ Cells need energy to survive.
☐ Carbohydrates are the main source of energy for the body.

3. **Different organ systems in the body have different roles.**

a) Which organ system brings oxygen into the body? Tick one box.

☐ digestive system
☐ respiratory system

☐ muscular skeletal system
☐ circulatory system

b) Which organ system brings glucose into the body? Tick one box.

☐ digestive system
☐ respiratory system

☐ muscular skeletal system
☐ circulatory system

c) Which organ system transports glucose and oxygen around the body? Tick one box.

☐ digestive system
☐ respiratory system

☐ muscular skeletal system
☐ circulatory system

Aerobic Respiration

1. Use some of the words from the box to fill the gaps in the sentences below.

| glucose | energy | chemical | reaction | conkers | cell | molecules |

Respiration is a chemical .... that happens in every ....

In respiration, ... is broken down to form new ....

This process releases .... , which is used for all the other ....

reactions that keep you alive.

2. Aerobic respiration can be described using a word equation.
Fill in the gaps to complete the word equation for aerobic respiration.

glucose + ... $\longrightarrow$ .... + ...

3. Look at the activities below.

a) Tick the activities that you think only involve aerobic respiration.

A ☐ B ☐ C ☐

D ☐ E ☐ F ☐

b) Explain why you have ticked those activities.

....

....

Aerobic Respiration

4. Ed is doing an experiment to look at respiration in woodlice. He sets up two tubes as shown.

a) Why hasn't Ed put any woodlice into tube B?

....

b) What would you expect to happen to the oxygen concentration in each tube?

....

....

PRACTICAL

tube A   tube B

rubber bung

woodlice

metal gauze

limewater

c) Limewater turns cloudy if carbon dioxide is present. What results do you expect for each tube? Tick one box.

☐ tube A cloudy, tube B cloudy   ☐ tube A not cloudy, tube B not cloudy

☐ tube A cloudy, tube B not cloudy   ☐ tube A not cloudy, tube B cloudy

5. Latika has made a flow diagram of how a car works.

If there's enough oxygen, a spark breaks bonds in the fuel and energy is released.

The energy is transferred to the kinetic energy store of pistons, which move and cause the crankshaft to rotate.

Water and carbon dioxide are also released.

The turning motion of the crankshaft is used to turn the wheels and the car moves.

SCIENCE IN ACTION

SUPREME

Latika thinks that this process is similar to respiration in humans.

a) In respiration, what is the 'fuel'?

....

b) Give one way the process shown is similar to respiration in humans.

....

....

c) Give one way the process shown is different from respiration in humans.

....

....

....

Anaerobic Respiration

1. There are two types of respiration — aerobic and anaerobic.

   a) Complete the word equation below for anaerobic respiration in plants
   and microorganisms.

   glucose ⟶ .... + ...

   b) What is produced during anaerobic respiration in animals?

   ....

   c) What is the difference between aerobic and anaerobic respiration in terms of:

   i) the reactants?

   ....

   ....

   ii) the amount of energy released?

   ....

   ....

2. Plant root cells need to respire just like all plant cells.

   a) Circle the correct answers to complete the passage below.

   In normal conditions spaces in the soil are filled with air. This means root cells can

   respire **aerobically / anaerobically**. If there is prolonged heavy rainfall, soils can

   become waterlogged. This means the spaces in the soil fill up with water. When this

   happens, root cells have to respire **aerobically / anaerobically**.

   b) Mangrove trees grow along shores and rivers.
   They are flooded twice a day by the tides.
   Many mangroves trees grow pencil-like roots,
   that stick out of the wet ground. How do you
   think this adaptation helps the mangrove trees?

   pencil-like root   trunk

   root
   system

   ....

   ....

   ....

Anaerobic Respiration

3. Emilia is doing an experiment to find out about yeast fermentation. She places some yeast in warm water in an open bottle.

PRACTICAL

a) What else will she need to add to the bottle to make sure the yeast can respire?

....

b) Emilia then attaches a balloon to the mouth of the bottle. What do you expect to happen to the balloon? Explain your answer.

....

....

....

....

Emilia says: (This experiment helps to show you why bread rises and why beer is fizzy.)

c) Explain how the experiment helps to show this.

....

....

....

....

d) Emilia wants to extend her investigation to find out whether temperature affects yeast fermentation. Describe a method she could use to investigate this. Include the variables she will need to control.

....

....

....

....

How did you do?

It might have taken a lot of energy to get through all that, but you made it. By now, you should:

- [ ] Know that respiration breaks down glucose and releases energy.
- [ ] Understand the differences between aerobic and anaerobic respiration.
- [ ] Know the word equations for aerobic and anaerobic respiration.
- [ ] Know how fermentation is used in brewing and breadmaking.

Topic 15 — Photosynthesis

Plants making food — a genius idea. I can just picture kitchens full of sunflowers wearing chef hats...

Learning Objectives

1. Know that plants make their own food (glucose) via photosynthesis.
2. Know that in photosynthesis, light energy is needed to convert carbon dioxide and water into oxygen and glucose.
3. Know how different plant organs are adapted to get the resources needed for photosynthesis.
4. Know what stomata are and understand their role in gas exchange in plants.
5. Understand why nearly all life on Earth is dependent on photosynthesis.
6. Understand how the rate of photosynthesis may be affected by changes in the environment.

Before you Start

1. Circle the correct word to complete each of the following sentences.

   a) A plant's **roots** / **leaves** take in water.

   b) Water travels **up** / **down** a plant.

2. Which of the following can plants not survive without? Circle your answer(s).

   people   lungs   nutrients   wifi

   water   light   air

3. Food is something that can be used as an energy source.
   Which of the following is true about plants and food? Tick one box.

   ☐ Plants get their food from the soil.   ☐ Plants absorb food into their leaves.

   ☐ Plants make their own food.   ☐ Plants don't need food.

4. The diagram on the right shows a leaf cell.

   a) What is the name of the structure labelled A?

   ....

   b) What is the role of the structure labelled A?

   ....

Plant Nutrition

1. Use words from the box below to complete the sentences that follow.

carbohydrate	cellulose	thermal	energy	respiration
protein	light	glucose	cake	photosynthesis

Plants use .... energy to help them make food. The food that plants

make is a type of .... called .... The process

by which plants make their own food is called .... Plants use the

food they make in this process to transfer .... to their cells.

2. Ameer has a green plant in a pot of damp soil.

SCIENCE IN ACTION

a) Ameer puts his plant in a dark cupboard and closes the cupboard door.

   i) Why won't the plant be able to make its own food while it's in the cupboard?

   ....

   ii) Ameer leaves his plant in the cupboard for two days. When he takes it out,
   it's still alive. Explain why the plant didn't die while it was in the cupboard.

   ....

   ....

   ....

   ....

b) James has the same type of plant as Ameer. He wants to have a competition with Ameer
   to see whose plant can grow the biggest.

   i) Ameer adds some fertiliser to his plant's soil.
   Explain how this could help Ameer to win the competition.

   Fertiliser contains mineral nutrients.

   ....

   ....

   ii) Ameer thinks that the more of its own food the plant can make, the more it will grow.
   Explain why he is correct.

   ....

   ....

Photosynthesis Basics

1. Photosynthesis is a chemical process, so it has reactants and products.

a) i) Complete the table below to show the reactants and products of photosynthesis, as well as things that are needed but are not changed in the reaction. Use words from the box below.

| carbon dioxide | glucose | water | chlorophyll | oxygen | sunlight |

Reactants	Products	Other things needed
1.	1.	1. ....
2.	2.	2. ....

ii) Use your completed table to write the word equation for photosynthesis in the box below.

b) Plants aren't the only organisms that carry out photosynthesis. Name another type of organism that can photosynthesise.

....

2. The diagram below shows the roots of a plant branching into the soil.

a) How does having branched roots benefit photosynthesis?

....

....

....

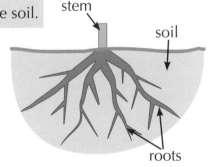

b) The upper parts of trees are also branched. Suggest how this benefits photosynthesis.

....

....

....

....

Photosynthesis Basics

3. Leaves are specially adapted to allow them to get everything they need for photosynthesis. The diagram below shows a cross-section of a leaf.

a) Explain why it is a good adaptation for photosynthesis for layer A to have more chloroplasts than layer B.

upper surface

Budge along a bit guys.

A

B

air space

lower surface

....

....

....

....

....

b) How do air spaces help the leaf in photosynthesis?

....

c) Leaves are often thin. Suggest how this helps a plant to maximise photosynthesis.

....

....

....

4. Ray investigated the leaves of a plant. He cut a leaf off a plant and covered one side of it in clear nail varnish and waited for it to dry. He then peeled the nail varnish off — an impression of the leaf had been created on the nail varnish. When he looked at the layer of nail varnish through a microscope, Ray could see tiny holes in amongst the leaf cells.

a) i) What is the name of the holes Ray could see?

....

ii) Describe how these holes are involved in photosynthesis.

....

....

b) Did Ray put nail varnish on the upper surface or lower surface of the leaf? How do you know?

....

....

Photosynthesis Basics

c) Ray's teacher says that if he had cut the leaf off the plant at night rather than during the day, the holes would have been closed. Explain why this could be true.

....

....

....

d) Ray also noticed the leaf had several 'veins', as shown on the diagram below. Suggest how these veins are involved in photosynthesis.

....

....

....

....

Ray's leaf impression

veins

5.   Isla is talking to Jake about a science-fiction film she watched.

Isla: At the beginning of the film, a cloud of black dust started surrounding the Earth, so no light could reach us. By the end of the film, there was almost no life left on Earth. That could happen in real life if it was dark all the time. It was really creepy.

Jake: That's so far-fetched, it's ridiculous. Even if all the light was blocked out from Earth, there's no way that almost everything would die.

A Dusty End

Do you agree with Isla or Jake about whether the outcome of the film could be true? Explain your answer.

....

....

....

....

....

....

....

....

Investigating Photosynthesis

1. Mia wants to show that leaves need chlorophyll for photosynthesis. She plans to use iodine as she knows that this turns from its normal orange-brown colour to blue-black in the presence of starch. She also knows that plants can store the excess glucose they produce as starch.

She conducts an experiment using a plant with variegated leaves (leaves that have both green and non-green parts). This is the method she used:

1. Put the plant under bright light for a few days.

2. Remove a leaf and sketch it to show the green and non-green areas.

3. Put the leaf in boiling water to remove its waxy coating.

4. Put the leaf in a test tube with some ethanol and place in a water bath for a few minutes. This removes the chlorophyll as it dissolves into the ethanol.

5. Wash the now white leaf in cold water and then cover it in iodine.

6. After a few minutes, draw another sketch of the leaf.

a) Why do you think Mia chose to use a variegated leaf in this experiment?

....

....

b) On the right is a sketch that Mia drew of her leaf before the experiment.

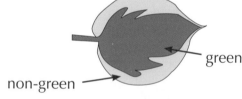

i) Which of the diagrams below do you think shows her leaf at the end of the experiment? Circle the letter of your choice.

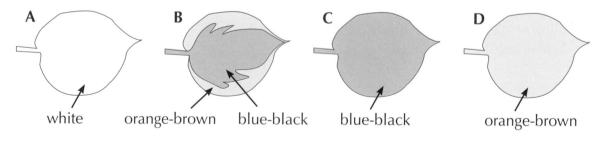

ii) Explain why you picked the leaf you did in part i).

....

....

....

....

c) Suggest one way that Mia could make the results of her experiment more reliable.

....

Investigating Photosynthesis

2. Sunita is trying to get the best conditions in her greenhouse to grow cucumbers.

a) Sunita is concerned about the temperature in her greenhouse being too high. She looks on the internet and finds the results of an investigation that measured the rate of photosynthesis in cucumber plants kept at different temperatures. In the conclusion of the report it says, "our results show that cucumbers grow best at around 27 °C, but don't grow at temperatures as high as 45 °C."

'As cool as a cucumber' I am not.

i) Complete the following sentence:

To investigate the rate of photosynthesis, the amount of .... the cucumber plants gave off over time could have been measured.

ii) Based on the conclusion of the report, sketch a line on the graph on the right to show how temperature may affect the rate of photosynthesis in cucumbers.

b) Other than temperature, suggest two environmental conditions that Sunita could control in her greenhouse to maximise the rate of photosynthesis.

1. ....

2. ....

rate of photosynthesis

27 °C   45 °C

temperature (°C)

c) Sunita notices that the fertiliser she uses doesn't contain magnesium. Magnesium is needed to make chlorophyll. Explain how using this fertiliser might affect the growth rate of her cucumber plants.

....

....

....

How did you do?

No matter what the weather, it's good to know that plants are working hard providing food for us all. By now, you should:

☐ Know that plants use photosynthesis to make their own food.

☐ Know what is needed for photosynthesis to happen and what is produced.

☐ Know how plants are adapted for photosynthesis.

☐ Know what stomata are and their role in gas exchange.

☐ Understand why nearly all life on Earth is dependent on photosynthesis.

☐ Understand what factors can affect the rate of photosynthesis.

 ☐ ☐ ☐

Topic 16 — Inheritance

Phew, you've nearly made it all the way to the end. Just one topic left to go. Get stuck in — it's a good 'un.

Learning Objectives

1. To understand the relationship between DNA, chromosomes and genes.
2. To know how the structure of DNA was discovered.
3. To know how DNA is passed from parents to offspring.
4. To understand how characteristics are inherited.

Before you Start

1. **The diagram on the right shows a plant cell.**

   a) What is the name of Structure A? ....

   b) Which of the following statements about Structure A is true? Tick the correct box.

   ☐ It is the site of most chemical reactions in the cell.

   ☐ It contains genetic material.

   ☐ It holds the cell together.

2. **Circle the correct words to complete the sentences below.**

   During sexual reproduction, the **nucleus** / **cell membrane** / **vacuole** of

   a male sex cell **combines with** / **replaces** the nucleus of a female sex cell.

   In animals, male sex cells are called **sperm** / **eggs** / **pollen** and female sex

   cells are called **sperm** / **eggs** / **bacon**. Male and female sex cells can also

   be called **embryos** / **gametes**.

3. **Look at the pictures of cats below.**
   Draw lines between each set of parents and their kitten.

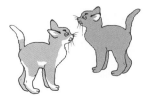

DNA

1. The diagram below shows how genetic material is arranged in a cell.

a) Label the diagram using the words below. Use each of the words only once.

DNA　　　　**Chromosome**　　　　**Gene**　　　　**Nucleus**　　　　**Cell**

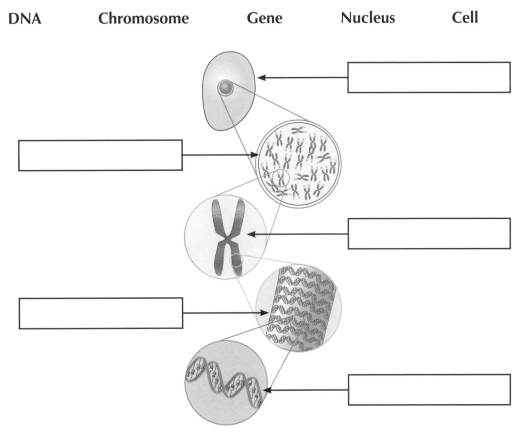

b) i) Tick any of the following statements that are <u>not</u> correct.

☐ A gene is bigger than a chromosome.

☐ Chromosomes are made up of DNA and contain many genes.

☐ A chromosome is a short section of DNA.

☐ A gene is a short section of a chromosome.

ii) Write out the corrected versions of any statements you ticked in part i).

....

....

c) An organism's genetic material controls many of its characteristics.
Which statements below are true? Tick two boxes.

☐ One chromosome controls one characteristic.

☐ One chromosome controls many characteristics.

☐ One gene controls one characteristic.

☐ One gene controls many characteristics.

DNA

2. In 1953, two scientists produced a model that showed the structure of DNA.

    a) What is DNA?

        ....

        ....

    b) What were the names of the two scientists that produced the model of DNA?

        ....

    c) In order to build their model, the scientists used evidence from X-ray photographs taken
        by other scientists.

        i) Name one of the scientists involved in taking
            the X-ray photographs.

            ....

        ii) Describe what the X-ray photographs showed.

            ....

            ....

    d) Omar built a model of DNA using strips of folded tinfoil and straws.
        A section of his model is shown below.

        Give one similarity and one difference between the structure of Omar's model
        and the structure of the model the scientists built in 1953.

        Similarity: ....

        ....

        Difference: ....

        ....

Inherited Characteristics

1. Tick the boxes to show whether the statements below about gametes are true or false.

True   False

a) Two gametes are needed to produce a fertilised egg cell. ☐ ☐

b) Gametes contain twice as many chromosomes as body cells. ☐ ☐

c) Gametes contain genes. ☐ ☐

2. Human body cells have 46 chromosomes.

The diagram below represents what happens during fertilisation in humans.
Complete the diagram by writing the name of each cell and the number of chromosomes contained within each cell.

Name: ....   Name: ....   Name: ....

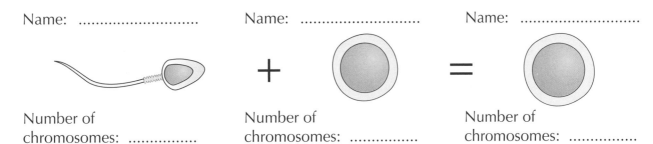

Number of chromosomes: ....   Number of chromosomes: ....   Number of chromosomes: ....

3. Lydia is doing a science project about reproduction in the animals that live on her farm. She's collected information about the number of chromosomes that are contained in cells at different stages during reproduction.

a) Complete the table below to show how many chromosomes are contained within the body cells of the parents, the gametes and the fertilised egg cells of each animal.

	Chromosomes contained in...		
	Body cell of parent	**Gamete**	**Fertilised egg cell**
Donkey		31	
Pig	38		
Goat			60

b) During the project, one of Lydia's pigs has a litter of 19 piglets.
How many chromosomes will there be in each body cell of the piglets?
Circle the correct answer.

1   either 9 or 10   19   38   76

c) Horse gametes contain 32 chromosomes. A hinny is an animal produced from mating a horse with a donkey. How many chromosomes are there in each body cell of a hinny?

....

Inherited Characteristics

4. A dragon's skin colour is controlled by a gene. One version of the gene (**B**) causes blue skin, and the other version of the gene (**b**) causes grey skin. The **B** version of the gene is dominant over the **b** version. This means that a dragon only needs to have one copy of the **B** version to have blue skin, but it needs two copies of the **b** version to have grey skin.

a) The dragons shown in the diagram breed together. Complete the diagram to show which versions of the gene for skin colour the offspring could inherit. Underneath the genes, write the colour skin that each offspring would have. The first one has been done for you.

Female bb

b) The dragons' offspring grow up living in a grassy meadow, where they hunt for toads. One of the offspring develops a mutation in the skin colour gene, which gives it green skin.

Male Bb

	b	b
B	Bb blue	....
b	....	....

i) What is a mutation?

....

ii) Do you think the mutation is likely to be harmful or beneficial? Explain your answer.

....

....

iii) Do you think it's likely that green-skinned dragons could become more common in the population? Explain your answer.

....

....

....

5. Olly is trying to find out which of his family members has broken a vase. He has the DNA from a hair he found on the broken vase analysed, as well as that of his wife Molly, identical twin daughters Polly and Holly, and dog Dolly. He hopes to compare the DNA from the hair to the DNA from his family members with DNA tests.

SCIENCE IN ACTION

Discuss whether you think Olly will be able to find out who the culprit is from the DNA tests.

....

....

....

....

....

Inherited Characteristics

6. A teacher is explaining heredity (the inheritance of characteristics) to his class. He uses different shaped magnets to represent chromosomes and displays them on the board. On the square magnet he draws a spot to represent a specific gene. A black spot is one version of the gene, and a blue spot is a different version of the gene. His display is shown below.

a) Use the teacher's display to help you explain how characteristics are inherited.

....

....

....

....

....

....

b) Explain why two siblings with the same parents won't look identical, but are likely to look similar.

....

....

....

....

....

....

How did you do?

There you go folks, the delights of dragon genetics. Very important stuff. By now, you should:

☐ Understand the relationship between DNA, chromosomes and genes.

☐ Know that DNA is passed from parents to their offspring during reproduction.

☐ Know how DNA's structure was discovered.

☐ Understand how characteristics are inherited.

Topic 16 — Inheritance

Mixed Questions

Now you've got through all that, it's time for some mixed practice.
Have a go at these without looking at your notes, to see what you know, and what you don't.

1. Chlorine is an element in Group 7 of the periodic table.

   a) On the periodic table, what is a group?

   ....

   1 mark

   b) What is another name for elements in Group 7? ....

   1 mark

   c) What is the chemical formula for hydrogen chloride? ....

   1 mark

   d) For the equation: $Fe + H_2SO_4 \rightarrow FeSO_4 + H_2$, write down:

   i) any substance that is a compound ....

   1 mark

   ii) any substance that contains only one element ....

   1 mark

   iii) all of the different elements present in this equation ....

   ....

   1 mark

2. Houses lose thermal energy through their walls by heating.
   One way energy is transferred by heating is conduction.

   a) Describe briefly how conduction transfers energy.

   ....

   ....

   1 mark

   Some houses have cavity walls. Cavity walls have an inner and outer wall with an air gap trapped in between. The trapped air reduces the rate of thermal energy transfer from inside the house to outside.

   b) What name is given to a substance that slows down the rate of transfer of thermal energy?

   ....

   1 mark

   c) Sometimes foam is added to the gaps in cavity walls. This is called cavity wall insulation. Other than convection, which type of thermal energy transfer by heating is reduced by the insulation?

   ....

   1 mark

Mixed Questions

3. An electromagnet is a coil of wire with electric current flowing through it. Mikesh has made an electromagnet using just a coil of wire attached to a battery. He is trying to make it as strong as he can, and is testing it by seeing how many paper clips he can pick up with it.

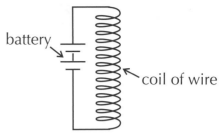

battery

coil of wire

a) Give **two** ways that Mikesh could make his electromagnet stronger.

1. ....

2. ....

2 marks

b) Scrap cars are often picked up by a crane operator using an electromagnet, which can be magnetised and demagnetised. Explain why a failure in the power supplied to the crane would be dangerous.

....

....

1 mark

4. Human cells generally have 46 chromosomes, which are usually shown in pairs. The only exception to this are the sperm and egg cells, which have 23.

a) What is a chromosome?

....

....

1 mark

b) In what part of the cells would you find the chromosomes?

....

1 mark

c) Why is it important that sperm and egg cells have only 23 chromosomes?

....

....

2 marks

d) Some people have a disorder called Down's syndrome. The diagram on the right shows the chromosomes in a person with Down's syndrome. Looking at the diagram, describe what you think may cause the disorder.

....

....

1 mark

Mixed Questions

Mixed Questions

5. Don is skating on a frozen lake. The total area of contact between both of his ice skates and the ice is 0.004 m².

   a) Calculate the pressure exerted by Don on the ice if he has a weight of 720 N.

      .... N/m²

      1 mark

   b) What will happen to this pressure if he uses skates that are twice as long? Tick the correct answer.

      ☐ It will not change   ☐ It will double   ☐ It will halve

      1 mark

   c) Don skates onto thinner ice. As he stands on the ice, it starts to crack. He decides to lie on his front and pull himself across the ice to safety. What effect will lying on his front have on the pressure that he exerts on the ice? Explain why.

      ....

      ....

      2 marks

   d) Don puts on a pair of spiked shoes so that they dig in and grip the ice. Explain, in terms of pressure, why the sharp spikes dig into the ice.

      ....

      ....

      1 mark

   e) Don spots a duck floating on the water in a hole in the ice. Describe in terms of weight and upthrust, why the duck is able to float.

      ....

      ....

      2 marks

6. The experiment below was carried out to test if carbon dioxide is needed for photosynthesis. Sodium hydroxide solution absorbs carbon dioxide.

   - First, the plant was left in darkness for 48 hours.

   - For the following 24 hours, the plant was placed in bright light with conical flasks attached to leaves A and B as shown on the right.

   - After this, leaves A and B were tested for starch.

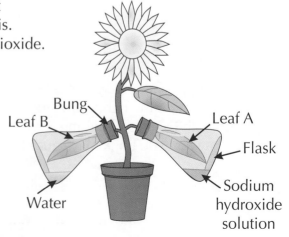

Bung
Leaf B
Leaf A
Flask
Sodium hydroxide solution
Water

Mixed Questions

a) Why was the plant placed in darkness for the first 48 hours?

....

....

1 mark

b) Why was leaf B placed in a flask with water?

....

1 mark

c) What is used to test for the presence of starch?

....

1 mark

d) When leaves A and B were tested for starch, what would
you expect the results to be? Explain your answer.

Leaf A ....

....

....

Leaf B ....

....

....

4 marks

7. Calcium carbonate can undergo a thermal decomposition reaction.
The symbol equation for the reaction is $CaCO_3 \rightarrow CaO + CO_2$

Use the periodic table at the back of the book to look up any chemical symbols you don't know.

a) Write down the word equation for this reaction.

....

1 mark

b) Explain what a thermal decomposition reaction is.

....

....

2 marks

A class was split into groups. Each group heated 1.00g of calcium carbonate in a crucible
for one minute and weighed the product. Their results are in the table on the next page.

Mixed Questions

Group	Mass before heating (g)	Mass after heating (g)
A	1.00	0.90
B	1.00	0.56
C	1.00	1.10
D	1.00	0.84

c) Which group has done something wrong? Explain your answer.

Group ....

Because ....

....

2 marks

d) Which group do you think heated their calcium carbonate
   most strongly? Explain your answer.

Group ....

Because ....

....

2 marks

e) One of the class, Kerry, wanted to work out the amount of energy required to break
   the bonds of the reaction. She knew that, for a certain mass of $CaCO_3$, the amount
   of energy released on bond forming is 1029 kJ/mol and that the overall energy
   change of the reaction is 178 kJ/mol.
   Calculate the amount of energy required to break bonds in the reaction for this mass.

.... kJ/mol

3 marks

f) On the axes below, draw an energy level diagram for this reaction.

2 marks

Answers

Topic 1 — Pressure and Upthrust
Page 3 — Before you Start

1

| mass | — | the amount of stuff in an object | | newtons (N) |
| weight | — | the force of gravity on an object | | kilograms (kg) |

2   **a)**   Weight = Gravitational Field Strength × Mass
        = 10 N/kg × 2 kg = **20 N**

  b)   Weight = Gravitational Field Strength × Mass
        = 3.8 N/kg × 2 kg = **7.6 N**

  c)   Weight = Gravitational Field Strength × Mass
        = 1.6 N/kg × 2 kg = **3.2 N**

3   Examples of forces: friction, air resistance, water resistance, reaction force.

Pages 4-6 — Pressure Basics

1   **a)**   True
  b)   False
        Pressure is measured in newtons per metre squared — newtons are the unit for force.
  c)   False
        Pressure is calculated by dividing force by area.
  d)   True
  e)   False
        The more force there is over a given area, the greater the pressure.

2   **a)**   Pressure = Force ÷ Area
        = 22 000 N ÷ 1.1 m^2 = **20 000 N/m^2**

  b)   Pressure = Force ÷ Area
        = 0.3 N ÷ 0.0005 m^2 = **600 N/m^2**

3   **a)**   Pressure = Force ÷ Area
        = 50 N ÷ 0.00001 m^2 = **5 000 000 N/m^2**

  b) i)   Area = Force ÷ Pressure
        = 600 N ÷ 37 500 N/m^2 = **0.016 m^2**

    ii)   If the total area of the nails in contact with Zac is 0.016 m^2, the number of nails must be 0.016 m^2 ÷ 0.00001 m^2 = **1600 nails**.

4   **a)**   Area = Force ÷ Pressure
        = 740 N ÷ 37 000 N/m^2 = **0.02 m^2**

  b) i)   4 × 0.07 = **0.28 m^2**

    ii)   Pressure = Force ÷ Area
        = 4900 N ÷ 0.28 m^2 = **17 500 N/m^2**

  c) i)   Pressure = Force ÷ Area
        = 740 N ÷ 0.4 m^2 = **1850 N/m^2**

    ii)   Snowshoes spread the force of a person over a larger area. So there is less pressure — the person is less likely to sink into the snow, making it easier to walk.

  d)   High-heeled shoes have a much smaller area in contact with the floor than normal shoes (or bare feet). This means that the force is spread out over a smaller area, so the pressure exerted is higher.
        This pressure could damage wooden floors.

5   **a)**   Force = Pressure × Area
        = 40 000 N/m^2 × 0.014 m^2 = **560 N**

  b)   The area that the force is exerted over will halve, as Eloise will be on one foot rather than two. This means the amount of pressure exerted will double, as the force will stay the same.

  c) i)   As the area in contact with his shoulders increases, the amount of pressure exerted will decrease, as the force is spread out over a greater area.

    ii)   Pressure = Force ÷ Area
        = 560 N ÷ 0.016 m^2 = **35 000 N/m^2**

  d)   The side of the hand has a much smaller area than the palm of the hand. If the same force is used to hit the block, the smaller area means that a greater pressure is exerted on the block, so it is more likely to break.

Pages 7-8 — Pressure in Fluids

1   **a)**   A substance that has no fixed shape, such as a gas or a liquid.

  b)   The weight of air above a surface.

  c)   As height above sea level increases, the weight of air above an object decreases, so the atmospheric pressure decreases.

2   less and less, decreases, decreases, more and more, increases, increases

3   As the depth of water in the bucket increases, the pressure in the water increases. This is because there is a greater weight from the liquid above. The greater pressure causes the water coming from the holes at the bottom of the bucket to travel further sideways.

4   **a)**   When the plane is in the air, the pressure in the crisp packet is greater than the air pressure outside the packet. The pressure in the crisp packet pushes outwards, causing it to expand.

  b)   As the plane descends, the air pressure on the outside of the bottle becomes greater than the pressure inside the bottle. This pressure pushes on the outside of the bottle, causing it to crumple.

5   **a)**   Pressure = Force ÷ Area
        = 100 N ÷ 0.001 m^2 = **100 000 N/m^2**

  b)   Force = Pressure × Area
        = 100 000 N/m^2 × 0.004 m^2 = **400 N**

  c)   The force at piston 1 will always be smaller than the force at piston 2 because it has a smaller area, and force is pressure multiplied by area. If the force at piston 2 is smaller than before, the force at piston 1 will also be smaller than before.

Pages 9-10 — Upthrust

1   increases, weight, downwards, upwards, upthrust, weight, float

2   **a)**   12 – 10.6 = **1.4 N**

  b)   float
        The lemon floats because its weight is a smaller force than the upthrust pushing it up.

3   **a)**   Water pressure increases with depth, so the force pushing upwards on the bottom of the beach ball is larger than the force pushing downwards on the top of the beach ball — the pressure causes an overall upwards force (upthrust).

  b)   The weight of the deflated beach ball is greater than the upthrust, so it no longer floats.

4   **a)**   Pressure = Force ÷ Area
        = 72 000 000 N ÷ 3200 m^2 = **22 500 N/m^2**

  b)   E.g.

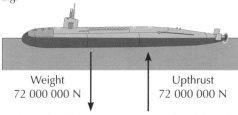

| Weight | Upthrust |
| 72 000 000 N | 72 000 000 N |

  c) i)   As the tanks fill with water, the weight of the submarine increases. When the weight of the submarine is greater than the force of upthrust, the submarine will sink.

    ii)   So that the submarine's weight can be decreased when it needs to resurface.

Answers

Topic 2 — Magnetism
Page 11 — Before you Start
1 False, True, False, False

2 You should have circled the steel can and the iron screw.

3 Attract, Repel, Repel

Page 12 — Magnetic Force
1 a) The magnetic force of the magnet acting on the ball.

b) Teresa is wrong. All magnets have two poles and magnetic materials are attracted to both poles.

c) The ball will move in a curve towards the magnet.
The moving ball will still be attracted to the magnet. The magnetic force of the magnet will cause the ball to change direction and curve towards the magnet.

2 a) Repel

b) Attract

Pages 13-14 — Magnetic Fields
1 a) The magnetic field created by the magnet.

b)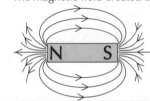

c) That the magnetic field around the magnet is stronger near the poles.

d) i) Further away from the magnet the magnetic force on the trolley is weaker. At 20 cm the force is too weak to overcome friction and move the trolley.

ii) The magnetic field is stronger near the poles of the magnet. After rotating the magnet, the trolley is closer to the north pole of the magnet and the force on the trolley is now great enough to make it move.

2 a) West
The compass needle is pointing north, so Egan must be facing west.

b) The Earth has a magnetic field, so the compass needle aligns itself with the Earth's magnetic field. This means it will always turn to point north.

c) The needle of Egan's compass is affected by the magnetic field created by Faye's compass needle.

3 a) E.g.

b) E.g.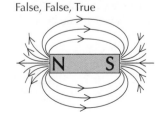

Topic 3 — Electromagnets
Page 15 — Before you Start
1 You should have circled the Earth and the compass.

2 False, False, True

3

Page 16 — Magnetic Effect of a Current
1 a)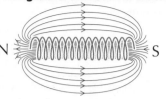

b) A solenoid

c) The magnet and the electromagnet would repel each other.
The magnetic field of an electromagnet behaves in the same way as one created by a permanent magnet.

2 a) When the switch is closed a current flows in the wire, creating a magnetic field around the wire. The compass needle is a magnet, so it is moved by the field around the wire.

b) The compass needle will move back to its original position. There will no longer be a magnetic field around the wire, so it will realign with the Earth's magnetic field.

c) The magnetic field around the wire will be weaker further from the wire. The compass is now far enough away that the force on the needle will be too weak to cause it to move.

Pages 17-19 — Using Electromagnets
1 a)

Electromagnet	For a clasp to keep a wallet closed.
	Picking up and dropping steel cans.
Permanent magnet	Pinning a note to your fridge.
	Lifting a maglev train off the tracks.

b) E.g. a very strong magnetic force is needed to pick up cars and electromagnets can be made to be much stronger than permanent magnets / electromagnets can be turned on and off, which make it easier to pick up and put down only the cars you want to move.

2 a) Using a magnetic core can make an electromagnet stronger.

b) i) Material 1 isn't magnetic, so using it wouldn't make Ronald's electromagnet any stronger / affect Ronald's electromagnet.

ii) Material 2 would stay magnetic after the current is turned off, making it unsuitable for picking up and dropping magnetic objects.

3 a) Mean number of paper clips:
10 coils — $(3 + 3 + 3) \div 3 = 9 \div 3 = $ **3**
20 coils — $(8 + 7 + 9) \div 3 = 24 \div 3 = $ **8**
30 coils — $(14 + 12 + 13) \div 3 = 39 \div 3 = $ **13**
40 coils — $(17 + 17 + 20) \div 3 = 54 \div 3 = $ **18**

Number of coils	Number of paper clips			
	Attempt 1	Attempt 2	Attempt 3	Mean
10	3	3	3	**3**
20	8	7	9	**8**
30	14	12	13	**13**
40	17	17	20	**18**

b) The more coils the electromagnet has, the stronger its magnetic field. The paper clips in the stronger magnetic field experience a greater force, so more could be picked up.

c) E.g. I agree with Aziz. Every time the number of coils was increased by 10 the electromagnet picked up 5 extra paper clips on average, so you only need two coils to pick up one extra paper clip.

d) E.g. increase the current flowing through the coil.

4 E.g. the current flowing through the wire causes a magnetic field to form around the coil. The magnetic fields of the wire and the permanent magnets exert forces on each other. These forces make the coil turn, which turns the fan.

5 a) When the switch is closed current flows through the electromagnet and a magnetic field is produced. The iron arm is magnetic and is attracted towards the electromagnet.

b) The contacts are pulled apart, which will break the circuit.

c) When the iron arm springs back, the contacts touch, turning the electromagnet back on, which moves the arm again. The cycle will repeat, causing the bell striker to repeatedly hit the bell.

Topic 4 — Work
Page 20 — Before you Start
1 B

2 using a screwdriver
Jodie could use the screwdriver as a lever to prise the lid off the paint tin.

3 distance: m, force: N, mass: kg, weight: N
Weight is a type of force. It's the force of gravity pulling downwards on a mass.

4
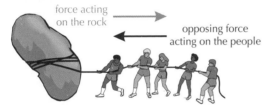
force acting on the rock

opposing force acting on the people

For every force that is exerted on object A by object B, there is an equal and opposite reaction force that object A will exert on object B.

Pages 21-22 — Work Done and Energy Transfer
1 a) The work done is the amount of energy transferred when a force moves an object.

b) Yes. The force the employee needs to use to push the boxes has increased, so the work needed to move the boxes will increase for the same distance.

c) The amount of work needed will increase. Work done is the amount of force used to move an object over a given distance. If the distance increases but the force remains the same then the work done will increase.

2

Journey	Total displacement (m)	Total distance (m)
Jolene walks 20 m from her house to her friend's house for a sleepover.	20	20
A runner runs one lap round a 300 m running track.	0	300
A cyclist cycles 750 m to the shops and then cycles back.	0	1500

Displacement is a measure of the distance travelled from the original location, so any movement that takes someone back to where they started results in zero displacement. Distance is the total distance travelled, no matter where the person travelling started or finished.

3 The car has the most work done.
Work done = force × distance
Car: 0.2 km = 200 m
　　1000 × 200 = 200 000 J
Bike: 200 cm = 2 m
　　200 × 2 = 400 J
Plane: 4000 × 4 = 16 000 J

4 Work done = force × distance
Distance = work done ÷ force = 12 ÷ 4 = **3 m**

5 E.g. The electric motor is applying a force to the rubber band which causes the wheel to turn. This applies a force to the load which causes the load to raise up a certain distance.
Remember that work done = force × distance, so the motor must be applying a force over a distance to be doing work.

Pages 23-25 — Levers, Pulleys and Wheels
1 turning force: a force that causes an object to turn.
moment: the turning effect of a (turning) force.

2 E.g. Wheels reduce friction so there's a smaller force acting against the movement of Ryan's suitcase than against Joe's suitcase. So Ryan will need to use a smaller force to pull his suitcase the same distance.

3 a)
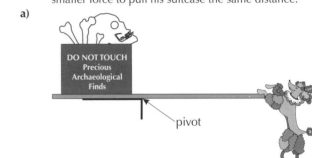
DO NOT TOUCH
Precious Archaeological Finds

pivot

b) The box will move upwards / in the opposite direction to the force applied by Cleo.

c) input, output

d) No. The further from the pivot that the force is applied, the greater the moment/turning force on the lever, so Spot is wrong.

4 Spanner B. It has a longer handle so Paula can apply a force further away from the nut/pivot. This will increase the moment/turning force so the nut will be easier to turn.

5 a) E.g. The work done by the input force has to be the same as the work done by the output force. So if the size of the input force decreases, the distance it acts over has to increase.

b) i) E.g. It requires a large force/a force equal to the weight of the load to raise the load 1 m.

ii) E.g. It requires the rope to be pulled a long distance to raise the load 1 m.

Topic 5 — Thermal Energy
Page 26 — Before you Start
1 The particles are fixed in position. (**solids**)
The particles of a substance have more energy in this state than when it's a liquid. (**gases**)
Heating causes the particles to vibrate or move more. (**both**)

2 a) The metal cup.

b) colder

c) The tea is heating up the air over the cup.

3 Repeatedly moving back and forth.

Answers

Page 27 — Thermal Energy and Temperature

1   False, True, True.

2   **a)**   From the heated block to the chilled block / from left to right.

    b) i)   The transfer of thermal energy between the blocks, and between the blocks and the surroundings, will reduce the temperature difference between them. Eventually there will be no temperature difference between them, so the blocks will be at thermal equilibrium.

      ii)   No. The thermal energy of a block depends on its mass, temperature and material. At thermal equilibrium, the temperature and material of the blocks is the same. However, the mass of the bigger block is greater, so it will have a higher thermal energy than the smaller block.

    c) i)
      ii)

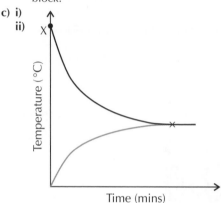

The blocks change temperature because thermal energy is transferred between them. As one block heats up, the other must cool down. This continues until they're the same temperature.

Thermal equilibrium is when there is no temperature difference between two objects. The point where the lines meet is when there is no temperature difference.

Pages 27-29 — Thermal Energy Transfers

1   convection — Occurs in fluids.
      conduction — Happens when particles collide with one another.
      radiation — Doesn't rely on the movement of particles.

2   **a) i)**   conducting
          made from thin metal

      ii)   E.g. The pipe needs to be conducting so that it transfers thermal energy quickly through it from the water inside the pipe to the lake. If it is made of thin metal, it can transfer thermal energy more quickly, as there is less material that the energy needs to be transferred through.

    b)   E.g.

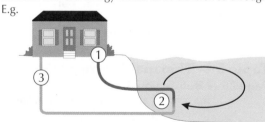

Convection currents occur in fluids. Fluids can be liquids or gases. Heated particles in the fluid will rise and then sink again as they cool down.

    c)   similarity: e.g. they both require particles to transfer thermal energy.
      difference: e.g. convection can't happen in solids but conduction can.

3   **a)**   A thermal conductor is a material that allows the quick / easy transfer of thermal energy through it.

    b)   E.g. Particles in the radiator with a lot of thermal energy collided with air particles to transfer thermal energy.

    c)   Hot air rises above cold air. As the radiator heats the air surrounding it, this air rises and is replaced by cold air. The cold air is then heated and the hot air, which no longer surrounds the radiator, cools. So the air by the radiator once again rises and the cycle continues. This constant cycle of moving air is the convection current.

    d)   The particles in the radiator have a lot of thermal energy so they vibrate a lot. When the person puts their hand against the radiator, the particles in the radiator collide with the particles in their hand, increasing the energy and movement of these. This increases the temperature of the person's hand.
      Conduction transfers thermal energy from the radiator to the person's hand as they are directly touching.

4   Thermal energy will be transferred from the heat source through the air into both potatoes. However, the potato with the skewer will cook faster as it also gets thermal energy transferred to it from the skewer, which is a better thermal conductor than the potato. As the metal skewer heats up, conduction transfers thermal energy along the skewer and into the middle of that potato.

Pages 30-31 — Reducing Thermal Energy Transfer

1   E.g. as air is a poor conductor of thermal energy, trapping pockets of it against the wearer will reduce the thermal energy that is transferred away from the wearer. The air around the body is warmed by thermal energy from the body and this warm air is trapped around the body by the jacket, keeping the body warm.

2   **a)**   convection: e.g. convection will cause warmer particles to rise in the liquid and air in the flask, but the stopper in the flask will stop them escaping.
      conduction: e.g. the vacuum between the edges prevents conduction from occurring because there are no particles in the vacuum for vibrations to be transferred to.
      radiation: e.g. the shiny edges reflect radiation waves back so fewer pass through.

    b)   No. The vacuum flask reduces the transfer of thermal energy between the liquid inside and the air outside. This could be thermal energy out from hot liquid in the vacuum flask or thermal energy in to cold liquid in the vacuum flask. This means it can keep things hot or cold.

3   E.g. the double-glazed window won't prevent all thermal energy from escaping. The air between the panes will conduct less heat than a pane of glass, but will still conduct some and the air will transfer heat by convection. The metal spacers will conduct some heat between the panes. There will still be some thermal energy loss by radiation.

Topic 6 — Wave Properties
Page 32 — Before you Start

1   False, True, False, True.

2

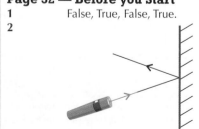

Answers

3 The sound waves produced by Ellen hit a surface and are reflected back to her (this is an echo).

4 The frequency of a wave is the number of waves that pass a point/are produced per second.

Pages 33-34 — Transverse and Longitudinal Waves

1 a) Transverse
   b) Transverse and longitudinal
   c) Longitudinal
   d) Transverse and longitudinal
   e) Transverse and longitudinal
   f) Longitudinal

2 a) i)

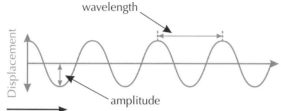

   ii) ─────────▶

   b) i) transverse wave
   ii) E.g. a light wave / water wave.
   c) E.g.

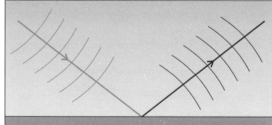

   You need to have drawn more waves in this diagram than in the diagram above.

3 transverse, perpendicular, longitudinal, Sound, air, energy

4 a) i) The waves will be reflected.
   ii)

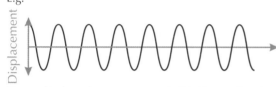

   b) The water particles in the wave will be moving up and down, perpendicular to the direction the wave is travelling in.

Pages 35-36 — Wave Properties

1 a) A transverse wave.
   b) E.g. they had different amplitudes.
   c) The waves will both travel at the same speed.
   d) Any two from: e.g. how taut the rope is / the distance the rope is being held away from the wall / the stillness of the rope before it is flicked.
   e) The wave will be reflected by the wall.

2 a) As the waves meet:

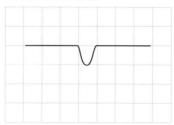

   After the waves meet:

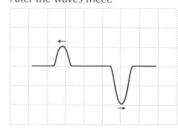

   b) Superposition

3 a) i) The waves move away from a fixed point through the water.
   ii) The amplitude of the ripples reduces as the waves travel outwards.
   b) The waves will combine so the crest will be twice as high.
   c)

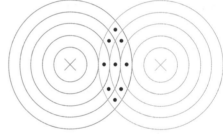

   The dots on the diagram show all the points where the trough will be lowest.

   d) At point A the crest of one wave will combine with the trough of the other wave, so the water will be level.
   e) The crests of the waves that are reflected back from the wall.

Topic 7 — Elements
Page 37 — Before you Start

1 <u>Metal</u>: ductile, magnetic, shiny, electrical conductor
   <u>Non-metal</u>: low density, dull, low melting point, insulator of heat, brittle

2 True, True, False, False
   Gas particles do move very quickly, but this doesn't mean that they're all reactive. Some gases are very unreactive.

3 Aluminium, copper, oxygen and bromine should all be circled.
   People often call fire, earth, air and water "the elements", but these are <u>not</u> chemical elements. You won't find any of them in the periodic table.

Pages 38-39 — Atoms and Elements

1 A, B and D should all be ticked.

2 Atoms are the **smallest** particles of an element that can exist. It took a long time for atoms to be discovered, because you can't **see** them directly. The first modern theory about atoms stated that all matter is made up of atoms and that there are **different** types of atom.

3 a) True   **b)** False   **c)** False
   d) True   **e)** False

Answers

4 Hiroki is wrong. He is right that elements are pure. However, elements can only contain one type of atom. So brass is not an element — it contains two elements mixed together (copper and zinc).

5 a) gallium — Ga, gold — Au, cobalt — Co, boron — B, copper – Cu
   b) i) N   ii) Br   iii) Na
   c) Water contains both hydrogen (H) and oxygen (O), so it can't be an element.
   d) i) carbon and iron should be ticked
      ii) magnesium and hydrogen should be ticked

Pages 40-43 — The Periodic Table

1 columns, right, groups, reactive
2 a) H, B, O, P, Cl and Xe are all non-metals.
   b) i) Rb / Mo / Xe   ii) Xe   iii) O
      iv) Cl   v) Rb
      Rb/rubidium is an alkali metal. Alkali metals react vigorously with water.
3 a) the alkali metals
   b) lithium
   c) The melting point decreases down Group 1.
   d) Any value below 39.3 °C.
      The actual answer is 28.4 °C.
   e) The boiling point will also decrease down Group 1.
4 a) Barium will react with hydrochloric acid to produce barium chloride and hydrogen gas. The reaction will be more vigorous than with calcium, because barium is below calcium in Group 2, and the reactivity of Group 2 metals increases down the group.
   b) Magnesium will also react with hydrochloric acid, producing magnesium chloride and hydrogen gas. This reaction will be less vigorous than with calcium, because magnesium is above calcium in Group 2 and therefore less reactive.
5 a) Any value between 9 and 22.6 g/cm^3
   b) The graph shows that for each group in this part of the periodic table, density increases down the group, so the density of Rh will be between that of Co and Ir.
6 a) Yes
      In a displacement reaction, the more reactive element displaces the less reactive element. Chlorine displaces bromine, and bromine displaces iodine. Therefore the order of reactivity from most reactive to least reactive is: chlorine, bromine, iodine, so the halogens become less reactive down the group.
   b) There won't be a reaction/nothing will happen. Astatine is below bromine in the periodic table, and the halogens become less reactive down the group. Therefore astatine is less reactive than bromine and won't be able to displace it from a salt solution.
7 a) silver
   b) E.g. chlorine is a gas at room temperature, krypton is a noble gas and bromine is a liquid. Therefore none of these are solids at room temperature, so they can't be used to make teeth. Lithium is in Group 1 so is highly reactive and therefore unsuitable for making teeth. Iron is a transition metal and less reactive, but rusts when in contact with oxygen and water. So over time an iron tooth would corrode.
      Silver is a solid at room temperature, very unreactive and doesn't corrode. Therefore it is the most suitable for making the teeth.
8 a) neon
   b) E.g. J can't be chlorine as chlorine displaces iodine from an iodine salt solution. Xenon is a noble gas, so it is unreactive. So J must be xenon.

Topic 8 — Compounds
Page 44 — Before you Start

1 Sc, Br, Cl$_2$, Co, O$_3$
   Some elements occur naturally as molecules (e.g. Cl$_2$, O$_3$, H$_2$). They're still elements, though, as they contain only one type of atom.
2 **Atom** — A very small particle. **Element** — A substance that contains only one type of atom.
   Mixture — Something made up of two or more substances that aren't chemically joined up.
3 carbon — element, air — mixture, seawater — mixture, paint — mixture, titanium — element

Pages 45-49 — Molecules and Compounds

1 a) True
   b) False
      It isn't easy to turn a compound back into its elements — you usually need to supply a large amount of energy to do this.
   c) True
   d) False
      Only elements can be found in the periodic table.
   e) True
   f) False
      Molecules must contain at least two atoms, but the atoms don't have to be different. Elements can exist as molecules.
2 a) B and C
   b) D and F
   c) four
      A and E show pure elements. D and F show pure compounds.
   d) A, D and F
   e) C
      Diagram C shows a mixture of two molecules. One of the molecules has two atoms of the same element, so this could be N$_2$. The other molecule has two different elements, so this could be CO.
3 a) hydrochloric acid + iron → **iron** chloride + **hydrogen**
   b) E.g. she should have worn a lab coat/goggles/gloves.
   c) i)

filter paper
funnel
beaker

      ii) Fiona could pour the mixture through the filter paper and funnel. The iron pieces will be collected on the filter paper, while the water will pass through the filter paper into the beaker below.
      iii) Because the iron in the beaker containing acid will have reacted to form iron chloride, which is a compound that dissolves in water. The dissolved iron in iron chloride will pass through the filter paper, so it can't be separated using filtration.
   d) Fiona's method won't work because iron iodide will have a different melting point to iron and iodine.
4 a) one
   b) magnesium sulfate
   c) CaSO$_4$
   d)

Name of Element	Number of Atoms
sulfur	1
oxygen	1
bromine	2

5 a) A molecule is two or more atoms joined together by chemical bonds.

Answers

b) NCl₃

   *"tri" means three, and "chloride" means that chlorine atoms
   are involved — so there must be three chlorine atoms in the
   molecule.*

c) Vincent's reasoning is wrong (in fact, nitrogen
   trichloride is a liquid at room temperature).
   Compounds rarely have the same properties as the
   elements that make them up.

6 **a)** E.g. two elements have reacted to form one product,
   therefore the product must contain both of the elements.

b) i) Any value between –10 °C and 5 °C.

   *The particle diagram at –10 °C shows a solid, and the particle
   diagram at 5 °C shows a liquid. Therefore the melting point of
   nitrogen dioxide will be between those two temperatures.*

   ii) E.g.

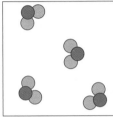

   *45 °C is above the boiling point of nitrogen dioxide (21 °C), so
   it will be a gas. The particles will be spread out and will be free
   to move in all directions.*

7 **a)** carbon, hydrogen, chlorine

b) i) E.g. chloroform is a liquid.

   ii) E.g. solvents need to be liquids. Carbon is a solid at
   room temperature, and hydrogen and chlorine are
   gases. Therefore a mixture of these elements would not
   contain a liquid.

   *Remember, solvents are substances which can be used to
   dissolve solids.*

8 **a) i)** neither Grace nor Erica

   ii) Grace is wrong because O₂ is not a compound. Both
   atoms in the molecule are of the same element, so O₂
   is an element. Erica is wrong in thinking that pure
   substances can only contain atoms from one element.
   Pure substances can be <u>either</u> elements or compounds
   (just with nothing else mixed in).

   *A pure substance is something that can't be separated into
   anything simpler without a chemical reaction — basically,
   anything that <u>isn't a mixture.</u>*

b) In a chemical reaction, the reactants rearrange to form
   the products. All the atoms from the reactants must end
   up in the products. The atoms present in the reactants
   are 2 O, 2 H, 1 Li and 1 Cl. In the first product the
   atoms present are 1 O, 1 H and 1Cl. This leaves 1 O,
   1 H and 1 Li atoms to form the product. So, since the
   other product contains more than one element, it must
   be a compound.

c) KClO

   *Sodium, lithium and potassium are in the same group of
   the periodic table (Group 1). Lithium and sodium form
   hypochlorites with the formulas LiClO and NaClO, so it is
   likely that potassium will follow this pattern.*

Pages 50-51 — Ceramics, Polymers and Composites

1 compound, thousands, repeating, natural, bonded,
   carbon

2 CONCRETE — composite — a mixture of sand and
   gravel embedded in cement, NYLON — polymer — a
   plastic that is soft and flexible, PORCELAIN — ceramic
   — a brittle material that is an insulator of heat.

3 **a)** man-made

   b) E.g. they're flexible and have a low density / are light.

c) E.g. ceramic materials are stiff and brittle. Therefore a
   ceramic bag wouldn't be flexible and would shatter if it
   was dropped. It would also likely be quite heavy.

4 **a) i)** ceramic

   ii) polymer/plastic

b) E.g. the advantages of using glass are that it is stiff, so it
   would make a sturdy greenhouse. It is also an insulator
   of heat, so would keep the greenhouse warm. Also its
   appearance doesn't deteriorate over time, so it would
   continue to let sunlight in, which the plants need.
   The disadvantages of using glass are that it is more
   expensive than PVC and is brittle so could shatter.
   The advantages of using PVC are that it is cheap,
   flexible and won't shatter. PVC, like glass, is a good
   insulator of heat so would keep the greenhouse warm.
   Also, it's easily moulded, which means it can easily
   be made into different shapes to fit the greenhouse.
   However the PVC could rip and will turn cloudy over
   time, so it would stop letting in as much sunlight, so
   would need to be replaced more often than glass.

   *It doesn't matter which one you picked for Jodie to use, so long
   as you can back up your choice with an explanation.*

c) i) a composite

   ii) E.g. fibreglass is a composite of both glass and plastic,
   so will combine the properties of both materials. For
   example, it will be stiff like glass and so will be strong,
   but will be more lightweight, due to the low density of
   the plastic.

Topic 9 — Types of Reactions
Page 52 — Before you Start

1 **a)** False

   *Only chemical reactions make new products. Physical changes
   only change the physical properties of a substance.*

b) False

   Non-metals can also be oxidised, e.g. carbon, sulfur.

c) True

d) True

e) False

   A more reactive metal will displace a less reactive metal.

2

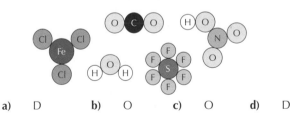

3 **a)** D   **b)** O   **c)** O   **d)** D

Pages 53-54 — Chemical Reactions

1 rearranged, reactants, before, products, after, conserved

2 **a) i)** magnesium oxide + hydrochloric acid → magnesium
   chloride + water

   ii) There has to be two molecules of hydrochloric acid to
   make sure that the reaction is balanced. There has to
   be the same number of each atom on each side of the
   arrow/equation.

b)

   $Mg + \begin{array}{c}Cu\\O\\S\\O\end{array}O \longrightarrow \begin{array}{c}Mg\\O\\S\\O\end{array}O + Cu$

c) $Mg + 2HCl \rightarrow MgCl_2 + H_2$

3 **a) i)** zinc + hydrochloric acid → zinc chloride + hydrogen

   ii) The reaction produces hydrogen gas, which can escape
   the beaker, causing the mass on the balance / mass of
   the beaker to decrease.

Answers

b) i) neutralisation reaction
  ii) zinc chloride and water
  iii) Mass is always conserved in a reaction and none of the products in this reaction are gases, so all of the products/mass will stay in the beaker.
c) i) Melting is a physical change so there would be no change in mass.
  ii) 3.44 g of oxygen.
     The difference between the mass of the product (13.44 g) and the mass of the reactant (10 g) is 3.44 g. Because there are no other products, and oxygen is the only other reactant, the difference must be equal to the amount of oxygen that reacted.
  iii) $4Ga + 3O_2 \rightarrow 2Ga_2O_3$

Pages 55-56 — Combustion and Thermal Decomposition

1   oxygen, chemical, hydrogen, carbon dioxide
2 a) i) thermal decomposition
   ii) E.g. there is only one reactant, from which two products are formed.
      Thermal decomposition reactions involve one reactant breaking down to produce at least two new products.
  b) Even though the reactant is not reacting with anything, a chemical change has taken place because new products have been formed.
  c) E.g. he could measure the total mass of the test tube before and after the reaction. If a gas is produced then the mass will decrease.
      The test tube was unsealed, so if a gas was given off then it would escape from the test tube, decreasing the mass.
  d) i) calcium oxide
    ii) copper oxide
    iii) lead oxide
3 a) methane + oxygen $\rightarrow$ carbon dioxide + water
  b) $2C_3H_8 + 5O_2 \rightarrow 2CO + 4C + 8H_2O$
  c) When the fuel is burned, the sulfur compounds are oxidised to produce sulfur dioxide. This then dissolves in clouds/rain to produce an acid, which falls as acid rain.
  d) water
     E.g. water is harmless. The combustion of propane can form a variety of products that are harmful pollutants (e.g. CO, CO_2 and soot).

Topic 10 — Chemical Energy
Page 57 — Before you Start
1 a) i) E.g. the heat in the air/room
   ii) The heat from the flame
  b) Because there is not enough heat in the air/room to heat the ice/water to boiling point but there is in the flame.
2 a) False
     Combustion reactions always involve oxygen.
  b) True
  c) True
  d) False
     Fuel stores energy in a chemical energy store.
3 a) $2Al + 3S \rightarrow Al_2S_3$
  b) $2Na + 2H_2O \rightarrow 2NaOH + H_2$
  c) $C_3H_8 + 5O_2 \rightarrow 3CO_2 + 4H_2O$

Pages 58-59 — Exothermic and Endothermic Reactions

1   transferred to, increases, increased, taken in from, decreases
2 a) A combustion reaction is an exothermic reaction because a substance gives out heat energy when it burns.

b) Thermal decomposition is an endothermic reaction because it requires heat energy for the decomposition to take place.
3 a) The reaction is exothermic because heat is given out to the surroundings.
  b) When the packet is opened, the iron is exposed to the air. This means that the oxidation can take place and heat is given out.
  c) $4Fe + 3O_2 \rightarrow 2Fe_2O_3$
4 a) i) The difference between the final water temperature and the initial water temperature
        = 49.9 °C – 24.8 °C = **+25.1 °C**
   ii)

Salt	Initial Water Temp (°C)	Final Water Temp (°C)	Exothermic or Endothermic?
ammonium nitrate	25.3	14.2	endothermic
calcium chloride	24.8	49.9	exothermic
sodium chloride	25.1	22.9	endothermic

b) i) ammonium nitrate
  ii) E.g. the final temperature would be lower, and the temperature would decrease more quickly.
  iii) calcium chloride
c) These heat packs are better because they can be reused (by boiling them in water), whereas the heat packs with salt and water cannot.

Pages 60-62 — Energy Levels and Bond Energies

1   A chemical bond is the force that holds atoms together in **molecules**. Energy is **transferred** when bonds are broken or formed. In a chemical reaction, bonds in the **reactants** are broken, which uses heat energy. New chemical bonds are formed in the **products**, releasing heat energy. Whether a reaction is exothermic or endothermic depends on the overall energy difference between bond breaking and forming.
2 a) In reaction B, the products have a higher energy than the reactants, so energy is taken in, meaning the reaction is endothermic. So the temperature would decrease rather than increase.
  b) The energy change for reaction A is bigger than the change for reaction C, so more energy will be released in reaction A.
  c)

Beaker	Temp Change	Exothermic or Endothermic?	Reaction A, B or C?
1	–4.4 °C	endothermic	B
2	+5.6 °C	exothermic	C
3	+7.1 °C	exothermic	A

3 a) A: –1276 kJ/mol
     B: +796 kJ/mol
     C: –892 kJ/mol
  b) Diagrams A and C. A combustion reaction is an example of an exothermic reaction, as it gives out energy to the surroundings. Diagram B shows an endothermic reaction.
4 a) $6CO_2 + 6H_2O \rightarrow C_6H_{12}O_6 + 6O_2$
  b) Energy change of reaction = energy required for bond breaking – energy released by bond forming = 15 204 kJ/mol – 12 520 kJ/mol = **+2684 kJ/mol**
  c) Endothermic
     The products have a higher energy than the reactants, so the energy change is positive, meaning the reaction is endothermic.
  d) Energy is required for the reaction to take place. Light energy is used by the plant to provide this energy.

Answers

5 **a) i)** fluorine
   ii) iodine
   b) i) In the forward reaction, the energy change is negative, so the products have lower energy than the reactants. In the reverse reaction, the products have a higher energy than the reactants, so the energy change is positive, meaning the reaction is endothermic.
   ii) Hydrogen iodide will decompose most easily because the reverse of the energy change will be +11 kJ/mol, meaning the energy required to break the bonds will be the least out of the four halogens.
   c) i) Energy change of reaction = energy required for bond breaking – energy released by bond forming = 1370 kJ/mol – 1856 kJ/mol = **–486 kJ/mol**
   ii) The formation of hydrogen fluoride is more exothermic as the energy change is greater/lower/more negative.

Pages 63-64 — Catalysts
1 **a)** True
   b) False
       The catalyst is not used up in the reaction, so the mass stays the same.
   c) False
       Different reactions require different catalysts. Most catalysts only work for one reaction.
   d) False
       Catalysts can be used for exothermic or endothermic reactions.
2 **a)** E.g. the factory can make another product that it can sell / the factory can reduce the amount of pollution it causes.
   b) E.g. it might be expensive/take a long time to install the catalysts and new equipment.
3 **a)** $2CO + 2NO \rightarrow N_2 + 2CO_2$
   b) Henry is wrong because catalysts are not used up in the reaction, so they don't need replacing. Linda is wrong because not every metal would work as a catalyst for this reaction.
4 **a)** $2H_2O_2 \rightarrow 2H_2O + O_2$
   b) i) Cylinder A is a control to show the reaction without the effect of a catalyst.
   ii) Lead oxide is the best catalyst, followed by manganese oxide. Iron oxide is not a very good catalyst as only a small amount of foam is formed.
   c) More energy is released than taken in. This negative energy change means that the reaction is exothermic. This means heat is given out, so the foam will be hot.

Topic 11 — Climate
Page 65 — Before you Start
1   The Earth's temperature is **increasing**.
2   Coal, Crude oil, Natural gas
3   Dead organisms are buried in the Earth and decay over millions of years.
4   hydrocarbon + oxygen → carbon dioxide + water
5 **a)** false
   b) false
   c) true
   d) false
   e) true

Pages 66 — Earth's Atmosphere
1 **a)** All the layers of gases that surround the Earth.
   b)
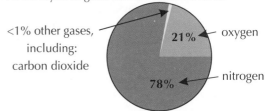
<1% other gases, including: carbon dioxide   21% — oxygen   78% — nitrogen

2 **a)** 79.32 + 5.31 + 11.42 + 1.69 + 2.17 = 99.91%. The total must add up to 100%, so the oxygen in Ulvertron's atmosphere is 100 – 99.91 = **0.09%**.
   b) E.g. the atmosphere in Ulvertron is very different to the atmosphere on Earth. There is only 0.09% oxygen, which humans need to survive, compared to 21% on Earth.

Pages 67-68 — Carbon Cycle
1 **a) i)** B
   ii) A and C
   b) i) E.g. it is released when the organisms respire.
   ii) E.g. some of the carbon is stored in the decomposers' bodies.
   c) E.g. they become fossil fuels which humans can extract from the Earth and burn, which releases carbon dioxide.
2 **a) i)** An area that absorbs and stores carbon.
   ii) e.g. oceans and soil
   b) E.g. it may have caused the carbon dioxide concentration to rise because it means there are fewer trees to absorb carbon dioxide from the atmosphere (for photosynthesis).
   c) The amount of carbon dioxide released when the biofuel is burnt is the same as the amount taken in when the plants used for biofuel were growing.
3 **a)** E.g. it dissolves into the water from the atmosphere.
   b) E.g. they're increasing it (as they're increasing the carbon dioxide concentration in the atmosphere).
   c) E.g. the student could measure the pH of the sea water in the beaker using the pH meter. They could then blow into the water through the straw and then measure the pH of the sea water again to see if it's more acidic.

Pages 69-70 — Climate Change
1 **a)** global warming, human, climate change
   b) Any two from: e.g. changing rainfall patterns / more droughts / more extreme storms / warmer temperatures.
2 **a)** Global warming is the gradual increase in the surface temperature of the Earth.
   b) e.g. carbon dioxide / methane
   c) B
       A is wrong because it shows radiation (waves) from the Sun being reflected before they pass through the atmosphere.
   d) The greenhouse effect is when energy from the Sun is transferred to the thermal energy store of Earth's atmosphere. Greenhouse gases reduce the thermal energy that's lost from the atmosphere through radiation, which helps to keep the Earth warm. As the level of greenhouse gases in the atmosphere increases, more heat is trapped by the gases, which causes the surface temperature of the Earth to increase — this is global warming.
3 **a)** Energy use per km
       = 18.5 kWh ÷ 100 = 0.185 kWh per km.
       So carbon dioxide per km = 0.185 × 350 g = **64.75 g**.

Answers

b) E.g. disagree — even though less carbon dioxide may be produced if everyone drove electric cars, there are still lots of other human activities producing greenhouse gases and contributing to global warming / CO_2 could still be produced when the electricity used in electric cars is generated.

4 E.g. I do. Graph B shows that the carbon dioxide concentration increased by almost 100 ppm between 1958 and 2018. Also, the textbook extract shows that, although CO_2 concentration does fluctuate, it didn't go above 300 ppm for hundreds of thousands of years before 1900. It's now been above this value since the early 1900s. Graph A shows that the world population was growing very rapidly at this time. Therefore, it seems possible that the increase in the number people on Earth has led to an increase in carbon dioxide concentration.

Just because two things are increasing at the same time, it doesn't mean that one is causing the other. More data would be needed on what else was affecting CO_2 level to be sure that humans are causing the increase.

Topic 12 — Earth Resources
Page 71 — Before you Start
1 A metal joined with another element by a chemical bond.

2 Elements in order of their reactivity towards other elements.

3 more, less, zinc, copper

4
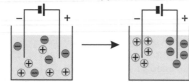

Page 72 — Extraction Methods
1 a) i) A natural metal or metal compound.
   ii) A natural rock from which it's worth extracting the metals/minerals it contains.
b) Because the metal is usually found in a compound in the ore, so it needs to be separated from the other element(s).
c) Iron is less reactive than carbon, so carbon will displace it in its compound. Aluminium is more reactive than carbon, so it will not be displaced by carbon.
d) i) electrolysis, compounds, elements, more, more
   ii) E.g. the positively charged aluminium atoms move to the negative electrode and the negatively charged oxygen atoms move to the positive electrode. This separates the aluminium from oxygen so that it can be collected.
   iii) E.g. it could be used to make cans / kitchen utensils / packaging / parts of buildings/vehicles.
e) E.g. the cost to mine the ore/extract the mineral/ transport the mineral from the mining location / How much pollution/environmental damage mining could cause.

Pages 73-74 — Recycling Resources
1 a) Processing a material so that it can be used again to make a new product.
b) i) E.g. disagree — Iona is reusing the cans, but they are not being processed into a new product so it isn't recycling.
   ii) E.g. avoid buying products that have lots of plastic packaging / buy things second-hand / buy recycled products / reuse more things that she buys.

c) The Earth's natural resources are limited. This means that the faster they're extracted, the faster they'll run out. So, recycling is important as it reduces the rate at which natural resources are extracted.

2 a) i) Palladium per phone: 0.016 g × £37.50 = £0.60.
   Silver per phone: 0.3 g × £0.38 = £0.11.
   Gold per phone: 0.035 g × £31.00 = £1.09.
   So total per phone from these metals is:
   £0.60 + £0.11 + £1.09 = **£1.80**.
   ii) £1 000 000 ÷ £1.80 = **555 556** phones.
b) There's a limited amount of metals in the Earth, especially the rare metals used in phones. So recycling means that there is less need to extract more of these metals, and they won't run out as soon.
c) E.g. phones could be made to last longer/be easier to repair, so that they don't have to be replaced as often as they currently are.

3 a) When they are recycled, metals aren't always in compounds so they don't need to be extracted, so less energy is needed.
b) Iron is a less reactive metal than carbon, so can be extracted using carbon. Aluminium is more reactive than carbon so has to be extracted using electrolysis, which requires a lot more energy than extraction using carbon. So more energy is saved when recycling aluminium.

Topic 13 — Breathing
Page 75 — Before you Start
1 a) True
   b) True
   c) False
   We breathe out the same volume of air that we breathe in.
   d) False
   We breathe in air and only about 21% of air is oxygen. (The rest of the air is made up of 78% nitrogen and 0.04% carbon dioxide.)
   e) True
2 lungs
3 B
4 Breathing is more difficult for her.

Pages 76-77 — Gas Exchange
1 a) trachea
   b) two tubes which carry air to the lungs
   c) bronchioles   **d)** diaphragm
   e) small air sacs found at the end of each bronchiole
   f) an arrangement of bones that surround the lungs
2 lungs, alveoli, oxygen, carbon dioxide, diffusion
3 a) Having lots of alveoli provides a large surface area so many gas molecules can diffuse in and out of the blood at once.
b) This means that each alveolus is very close to the blood supply, so gases diffusing in and out of the blood have only a short distance to travel.
4 a)
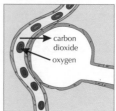

Answers

b)

BLOODSTREAM		ALVEOLUS	
Gas	**Conc.**	**Gas**	**Conc.**
Oxygen	LOW	Oxygen	HIGH
Carbon dioxide	HIGH	Carbon dioxide	LOW

ii)

	Starting Breathing Rate (breaths per minute)	Peak Breathing Rate (breaths per minute)	Percentage Increase (%)
Runner A	12	54	350
Runner B	8	32	300

c) Carbon dioxide is a waste product of respiration in body cells.

5 E.g. the efficiency of gas exchange will decrease, because the surface area of the alveoli has been decreased, so fewer gas molecules can diffuse in and out of the blood at once.

Pages 78-79 — The Mechanism of Breathing

1 a)

Diaphragm moves...	Ribcage moves...	Volume...	Pressure...
down	**up**	increases	**decreases**
up	down	decreases	**increases**

b) She's right.

2 a) i) the trachea
ii) the rib cage / chest cavity
iii) the diaphragm

b) E.g. the balloons are large, open spaces whereas the lungs are made up of millions of individual alveoli.

c) When the rubber sheet is pushed into the bell jar, the volume inside the bell jar decreases. This increases the pressure inside the jar so that it is higher than outside. This causes air to rush out of the balloons, so they deflate.

d) She is wrong because the balloons can be inflated due to changes in pressure in the bell jar. You can inflate the balloons by pulling down on the rubber sheet.

3 a) Lung volume is the amount of air that can be breathed in or out in a single breath.

b) E.g. Carlos' prediction, because as height increases, lung size should also increase and therefore lung volume will be bigger.

c) i) Carlos: 4600 + 4695 + 4550 = 13 845 ÷ 3 = **4615 mL**
Jane: 4580 + 4600 + 4650 = 13 830 ÷ 3 = **4610 mL**

ii) The results show that Carlos has a bigger lung volume than Jane. Carlos made the correct prediction.

d) Lisa is likely to be wrong because she is taller than Jane and therefore is likely to have a bigger lung volume than her.

Pages 80-81 — Exercise, Asthma and Smoking

1 a) E.g. because he's sensitive to animal hair and breathes it in.

b) E.g. the muscles around his bronchioles have contracted, and narrowed the airways.

2 a) 3 minutes, because that's when the runners' breathing rates started to increase.

b) 21 minutes
The run started at 3 minutes (when the runners' breathing rates increased) and ended at 24 minutes (when the runners' breathing rates started to decrease), so it lasted 24 − 3 = 21 minutes.

c) i) Runner A: 34 − 24 = **10 minutes**
Runner B: 29 − 24 = **5 minutes**

To work out the percentage increase in breathing rate, use: (peak breathing rate − starting breathing rate) / starting breathing rate × 100
Runner A: (54 − 12)/12 × 100 = 42/12 × 100 = 350%
Runner B: (32 − 8)/8 × 100 = 24/8 × 100 = 300%

d) i) stronger diaphragm

ii) Runner B, e.g. because they have a lower peak breathing rate. A person who exercises regularly is likely to have developed stronger breathing muscles/ diaphragm/intercostal muscles. This means their chest cavity will open up more when they breathe and they can get more air into their lungs in each breath, so their breathing rate when exercising won't get as high as people who don't exercise regularly.
A regular exerciser is also likely to have more/bigger alveoli, allowing more gas to be exchanged in each breath, so breathing rate is lower.

3 a) Because gas exchange in their lungs is less efficient, so it's harder to get all of the oxygen they need and harder still when doing exercise. If their breathing rate can't increase enough to supply the oxygen they need, they'll become out of breath.

b) Decrease, because if the efficiency of gas exchange is lower, there is likely to be less oxygen in the blood to be used in respiration.

Topic 14 — Respiration
Page 82 — Before you Start

1 All the pictures should be circled.
All living things need energy to survive.

2 Cells need energy to survive.
The body uses energy to move around.
Carbohydrates are the main source of energy for the body.

3 a) respiratory system
b) digestive system
c) circulatory system

Pages 83-84 — Aerobic Respiration

1 reaction, cell, glucose, molecules, energy, chemical

2 glucose + **oxygen** → **carbon dioxide** + **water**

3 a) The following should all be ticked: A, C, E, F

b) E.g. these activities are all fairly gentle, so the body will be able to get enough oxygen to the muscle cells so they can respire aerobically.

4 a) It is being used as a control tube. / To show that any changes are caused by the woodlice.

b) The oxygen concentration would decrease in tube A and stay the same in tube B.

c) tube A cloudy, tube B not cloudy

Answers

5 a) glucose

b) E.g. in the car the energy released from breaking down the fuel moves the pistons/wheels/car. In respiration, the energy released from breaking down glucose is used to move the body. / Oxygen is needed in both processes. / Carbon dioxide and water are produced in both processes.

c) E.g. in respiration the energy released is used for all the chemical reactions in the body, not just to move the body. In the car the energy released just moves the pistons/wheels/car.

Pages 85-86 — Anaerobic Respiration
1 a) glucose → ethanol + carbon dioxide

b) lactic acid

c) i) Aerobic respiration requires oxygen, whereas anaerobic respiration doesn't.

ii) Aerobic respiration releases more energy for every glucose molecule than anaerobic respiration.

2 a) aerobically, anaerobically

b) E.g. the pencil-like roots stay above the water so that they can take in oxygen from the air, allowing the root cells to respire aerobically.

3 a) sugar/glucose

b) E.g. the balloon will inflate. When yeast respire they produce gas/carbon dioxide. As the balloon is covering the mouth of the bottle, the gas/carbon dioxide will be trapped and so will start to fill the balloon.

c) E.g. yeast is used in bread making and brewing. The gas/carbon dioxide produced by the yeast respiring causes bubbles to form in beer, making it fizzy. In bread making, the gas/carbon dioxide produced makes air pockets form, which makes the bread rise.

d) E.g. she could repeat the experiment at different temperatures and time how long it took for the balloon to fill to a certain size. She would need to use the same size bottles and balloons. She would also need to use the same amount of yeast, water and sugar in each bottle.

Topic 15 — Photosynthesis
Page 87 — Before you Start
1 a) A plant's **roots** take in water.

b) Water travels **up** a plant.

2 Air, light, water and nutrients should be circled.

3 Plants make their own food.

4 a) chloroplast

b) To make food for a plant.

Page 88 — Plant Nutrition
1 light, carbohydrate, glucose, photosynthesis, energy

2 a) i) There isn't any light.

ii) Before the plant was put in the cupboard it may have stored some of the glucose it made in photosynthesis. The plant would have been able to use this glucose to stay alive/as an energy source while it was in the cupboard.

b) i) The plant will absorb mineral nutrients from the fertiliser through its roots and use them to build new tissue, which will mean it grows bigger.

ii) E.g. plants use glucose to build new tissue, which they need to do in order to grow.

Pages 89-91 — Photosynthesis Basics
1 a) i)

Reactants	Products	Things needed but not changed
1. water 2. carbon dioxide	1. glucose 2. oxygen	1. sunlight 2. chlorophyll

ii) carbon dioxide + water $\xrightarrow[\text{chlorophyll}]{\text{sunlight}}$ glucose + oxygen

b) e.g. algae

2 a) Being branched gives the roots a larger surface area. This means they're able to absorb more water, which is needed for photosynthesis.

b) The branches on the upper parts of trees are where the leaves are. Being branched means that the leaves are held out over a larger area, so they're exposed to more light. This means they can absorb more light energy, which is needed for photosynthesis.

3 a) Chloroplasts absorb the light energy needed for photosynthesis. Layer A is closer to the upper surface of the leaf than layer B, so is more exposed to light. Therefore having more chloroplasts means it can absorb more light, which maximises photosynthesis.

b) E.g. they allow carbon dioxide to move easily between leaf cells.

c) E.g. being thin means there's only a short distance for carbon dioxide to diffuse into all of the leaf cells, meaning photosynthesis can happen more quickly.

4 a) i) stomata

ii) They allow the carbon dioxide needed for photosynthesis to diffuse into the leaf, and the oxygen produced in photosynthesis to diffuse out.

b) The lower surface because stomata are only found on the lower surface of leaves.

c) E.g. at night there would be no light available for photosynthesis. This means the stomata may have closed as carbon dioxide isn't needed in the leaf.

d) E.g. the veins allow water to reach the leaf cells as they connect to the stem, which carries water up the plant. They also transport the glucose produced in photosynthesis away to other parts of the plant.

5 E.g. I agree with Isla. Plants and algae use light energy from the Sun to make glucose during photosynthesis. The energy from this glucose and the other molecules plants make from it, is passed from plants to animals when animals eat the plants. The energy gets passed on again when these animals are eaten by other animals. Photosynthesis also produces oxygen, which living organisms need for respiration/to survive. Without light, there'd be no photosynthesis so almost all organisms would lose their source of energy and there'd be less oxygen available. This could mean that almost all organisms on Earth might die.

Pages 92-93 — Investigating Photosynthesis
1 a) Only the green parts of the leaf will have chlorophyll in them, so it's easy to see whether chlorophyll is needed for photosynthesis.

b) i) B

ii) The green parts of the leaf can photosynthesise and so will have produced glucose and stored it as starch, meaning the iodine will have turned blue-black. The non-green parts aren't able to photosynthesise so the iodine will have remained orange-brown.

c) E.g. repeat the experiment using more leaves.

Answers

2 **a)** **i)** oxygen
ii) E.g.

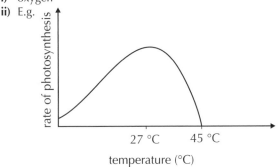

b) E.g. the light intensity and the carbon dioxide concentration.
c) E.g. the cucumber plants won't be able to make as much chlorophyll as they could if the fertiliser contained magnesium, so they won't be able to absorb as much light. This could mean they aren't able to photosynthesise as quickly, which could mean that their growth rate is slower.

Topic 16 — Inheritance
Page 94 — Before you Start
1 **a)** nucleus
b) It contains genetic material.
2 nucleus, combines with, sperm, eggs, gametes
3

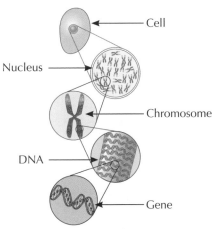

Pages 95-96 — DNA
1 **a)**

b) **i)** A gene is bigger than a chromosome.
A chromosome is a short section of DNA.
ii) E.g. a gene is smaller than a chromosome.
A chromosome is a long length of DNA.
c) One chromosome controls many characteristics.
One gene controls one characteristic.
2 **a)** DNA is the molecule that contains genetic information/ the chemical instructions for building an organism.
b) (James) Watson and (Francis) Crick
c) **i)** E.g. (Rosalind) Franklin / (Maurice) Wilkins
ii) They showed the basic structure of DNA/that DNA is a double helix.

d) Similarity: e.g. both models show that DNA contains two strands. / Both models show that DNA contains twisted strands. / Both models show that DNA contains strands that are joined together.
Difference: e.g. the scientists' model shows that the strands wind round each other/form a double helix, but Omar's model shows the strands side by side.

Pages 97-99 — Inherited Characteristics
1 **a)** True
b) False
Gametes contain half the number of chromosomes as body cells.
c) True
2

Name: sperm + Name: egg = Name: fertilised egg

Number of chromosomes: 23   Number of chromosomes: 23   Number of chromosomes: 46

3 **a)**

	Chromosomes contained in...		
	Body cell of parent	**Gamete**	**Fertilised egg cell**
Donkey	62	31	62
Pig	38	19	38
Goat	60	30	60

b) 38
c) 63
During reproduction, a horse gamete with 32 chromosomes will combine with a donkey gamete with 31 chromosomes. So each body cell of a hinny will have 32 + 31 = 63 chromosomes.

4 **a)**

	b	b
B	Bb blue	Bb blue
b	bb grey	bb grey

b) **i)** A change in DNA.
ii) E.g. beneficial, because green skin might help the dragon to be camouflaged in its grassy habitat, meaning it can hunt more successfully for toads.
iii) E.g. yes, because green-skinned dragons may be more likely to survive and reproduce, and pass on the DNA/ gene for green skin to their offspring. This could continue over many generations, meaning green-skinned dragons become more common.
5 E.g. everybody's DNA is different, so only one family member's DNA should match that of the hair. However, the exception to this is identical twins, who have identical DNA. So the DNA from the hair could match that of both Polly and Holly, meaning he might not be able to find the culprit from the DNA alone.
6 **a)** E.g. chromosomes come in pairs, and a baby inherits one copy of each chromosome from its mum and one from its dad. Chromosomes contain genes, which control different characteristics. So a baby gets one version of each gene from its mum and one from its dad. The different versions of genes it receives determines which characteristics in inherits.

Answers

b) Both siblings will have inherited all of their genes from the same parents, but they will have received a different mix of genes, meaning they don't look identical. However, it's likely that some of the genes one sibling inherited will be the same as the genes the other sibling inherited. This means they're likely to share some of the same genes that control appearance, resulting in them looking similar.

Mixed Questions
Pages 100-104

1 **a)** A column on the periodic table *[1 mark]*
  b) halogens *[1 mark]*
  c) HCl *[1 mark]*
  d) i) H_2SO_4, $FeSO_4$ *[1 mark]*
   ii) Fe, H_2 *[1 mark]*
   iii) iron/Fe, hydrogen/H, oxygen/O, sulfur/S *[1 mark]*

2 **a)** Thermal energy is transferred through vibrations that are passed from particle to particle. *[1 mark]*
  b) A (thermal) insulator *[1 mark]*
  c) conduction *[1 mark]*

3 **a)** Any two from: e.g. add more turns to the coil, increase the electric current through the coil, add a soft iron core. *[1 mark for each correct answer]*
  b) An electromagnet only attracts the cars if a current flows through it, so a power failure could cause the crane to drop a car *[1 mark]*

4 **a)** A structure containing tightly-coiled DNA/a long coiled up length of DNA *[1 mark]*
  b) The nucleus *[1 mark]*
  c) When the sperm fertilises the egg *[1 mark]*, the new cell still has 46 chromosomes *[1 mark]*.
  d) Having too many/47 chromosomes / having an extra number 21 chromosome. *[1 mark]*

5 **a)** Pressure = Force ÷ Area, so
  720 N ÷ 0.004 m² = 180 000 N/m² *[1 mark]*
  b) It will halve *[1 mark]*
  c) It will reduce the pressure *[1 mark]*, because his weight is spread over a larger surface area *[1 mark]*.
  d) The spikes have a very small surface area, so when Don's weight is put onto them they produce a large pressure to dig into the ice. *[1 mark]*.
  e) The force pushing downwards from the weight of the duck *[1 mark]* is equal to the force pushing upwards from the water (upthrust). *[1 mark]*

6 **a)** To get rid of all the starch from the leaves so that any starch present after the 24 hours has all been produced while the leaf was in the flask *[1 mark]*.
  b) E.g. to act as a control, to prove that it was carbon dioxide having an effect *[1 mark]*
  c) Iodine *[1 mark]*
  d) Leaf A would be negative/would not contain starch/ would go brown *[1 mark]*. The leaf would not have been able to absorb any carbon dioxide, so would have been unable to photosynthesise and produce starch *[1 mark]*. Leaf B would be positive/would contain starch/would turn black *[1 mark]*. The leaf could take in carbon dioxide and so could photosynthesise to produce starch *[1 mark]*.

7 **a)** calcium carbonate → calcium oxide + carbon dioxide *[1 mark]*
  b) A thermal decomposition reaction is where one reactant is heated *[1 mark]* and broken down into simpler/two products *[1 mark]*.
  c) C *[1 mark]*, because their sample has gained mass *[1 mark]*.

d) B *[1 mark]*, because their sample has lost the most mass/produced the most CO_2 *[1 mark]*.
e) The reaction is endothermic as it takes in heat *[1 mark]*, so the energy required will be more than the energy released *[1 mark]*.
So energy required = 1029 kJ/mol + 178 kJ/mol
                            = **1207** kJ/mol *[1 mark]*
f) E.g.

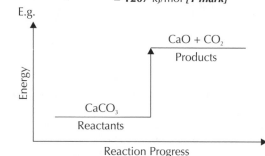

[2 marks for the complete diagram, otherwise 1 mark for putting the reactants at a lower energy than the products]